THE GUIDE HANDBOOK

by
Dorothy Crocker

Published by Girl Guides of Canada
Guides du Canada

ISBN 0-919220-00-2

Published by Girl Guides of Canada — Guides du Canada

Printed in Canada

First Edition — 1977

CONTENTS

CHAPTER FIVE/164

Jenny and Carol go camping; explore Treasure Island; play an exciting wide game; entertain the Brownies at campfire; and have a Guides' Own.

INBETWEEN FIVE/186

6

CHAPTER SIX/250

Jenny has a new neighbour; she and her friends look after four-year-old twins; the Guides decide to help clean up the river banks.

INBETWEEN SIX/266

CHAPTER SEVEN/290

The Guides have a breakfast hike and Court of Honour; Jenny and Carol are elected Patrol Leaders; Lori's unhappiness; Lori moves and becomes a Lone Guide.

INBETWEEN SEVEN/306

CHAPTER EIGHT/322

The Guides go winter camping to celebrate Thinking Day; "tour" the world's continents with food, games and activities; greet Thinking Day at midnight; talk about Rangers and Cadets; and survive an ice storm.

INBETWEEN EIGHT/341

INTRODUCTION

Have you ever folded a piece of paper like this,

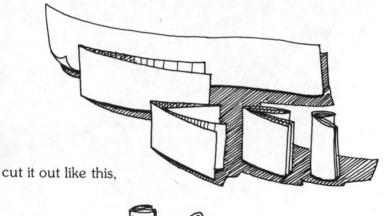

cut it out like this,

unfolded it, and found a row of paper dolls like this?

It's fun to do, and greatly amuses a small child you are trying to entertain.

But real people aren't like a row of paper dolls. Each person is different, special, unique.

You are *you*. Nobody else thinks or feels or acts quite the same as you do. Nobody else looks the same as you do; even if you have an identical twin, she isn't exactly the same.

You are, or soon will be, a Girl Guide. You will have over 75,000 sister Guides in Canada, and many, many more around the world in almost a hundred countries. Each of you is different.

It's time to pack you mental knapsack with what you need to know in order to be able to take part in the many exciting adventures that await you along the four paths of Discovery. It's a journey that will take you through your home, your community, outdoors and to camp and beyond into the wide world. Keep your Promise and Law ahead of you to guide you and you're all set. Follow the paths. Discover what *you* want to discover. This book is a story of some Guides who were discoverers. After each chapter of their story are Inbetweens to help you make your own discoveries.

Happy travels!

1

Dear Jenny,

The Girl Guide Company is happy you came up from Brownies. We are holding our next meeting on Monday, September 17, from 7 pm to 9 pm.

Please take off your socks and shoes and draw the outline of your feet on the paper enclosed. If you are right-handed, use your left hand. If you are left-handed, use your right hand. You may do it in the dark if you wish. Bring these with you.

Your friends,
The Guides

Two pieces of red construction paper fluttered out of the envelope. Jenny read the letter carefully. Draw your feet, maybe in the dark, and go to Guides? It was most decidedly mysterious!

Jenny had just flown up to Guides from the Brownie pack where she had earned her Golden Hand. The night of the Flying Up Ceremony was fun, especially when they pretended they were the first women to land on the moon, and wore papier-mâché space helmets designed by themselves. The Guides thought it was fun having the Brownies pretend the Guide company was the moon. Mrs. McKay, the Guide leader whom everyone called 'Captain' or 'Mrs. Mac', had laughed and said they could call it the Once-on-a-Blue-Moon ceremony.

The Guides had been nice to the Brownies, but they all looked so tall. Jenny was ten, and had got used to being one of the oldest Brownies. Now, suddenly, she felt very young. She knew only a few of the Guides and those only by name. She wasn't at all sure that she wanted to be a Guide after all.

But the invitation made her very curious. She wished that her best friend, Carol, had been a Brownie. The next day when she called for Carol to go to school, she showed her the letter. Carol was just as curious as Jenny. When Jenny asked her if she'd like to go to Guides with her, she said she would, if only to find out why she had to draw her feet.

"Are you sure it'll be all right?" she asked anxiously. "I wasn't a Brownie or anything, and the leader doesn't know me, and maybe they won't want me to come."

"Of course it'll be all right," said Jenny. "Anyhow, we mightn't like it and we can say we're just visiting to see what it's like. You could phone the leader and ask her, I guess, but . . ." she trailed off a little doubtfully. The Brownie pack had always been full and new girls had to wait to join. But perhaps Guides would be different. Still, she didn't want to take any chances. Carol was her best friend and she hadn't been looking forward to being in Guides without Carol.

On Monday after school they got some extra red paper. In Jenny's room they carefully outlined their feet. Jenny was left-handed, but was pretty good with her right hand. So many things were made for right-handed people that she had learned to use her right hand fairly well. Carol had trouble keeping the pencil in place with her left hand. It was a pretty wobbly outline.

"Well, it said we could do it in the dark," said Jenny. "Let's go in the clothes closet and shut the door and both do it in the dark. Maybe mine will be crummy and yours will be good then."

When they emerged from the closet and looked at their feet outlined on the paper, they discovered that both had drawn firm, clear outlines.

"Is that ever funny! Maybe we should try doing our homework in the dark. It might turn out right!"

After supper, they set out for the church hall in lots of time. They were excited and any fears they'd had were gone. It wasn't until they reached the door that Carol's earlier uncertainty returned. On the door was a sign with a picture of a Brownie man wearing a Guide beret and scarf. The sign read:

WELCOME BROWNIES!
COME INSIDE AND FOLLOW THE
ALPHABET. AT EACH LETTER TAKE
ONE ITEM OUT OF THE BOX.
EAT ONE PART OF THE CIRCLE THAT
HAS A GUIDE HAT IN THE MIDDLE.

"See, I told you! It's for kids who were Brownies. We should've phoned and asked if I could come." Carol was close to tears. "I'm going home."

Jenny was in a quandary. She wanted terribly much to go in, but she couldn't leave Carol. If only she had telephoned Mrs.

McKay and found out for sure if Carol would be welcome!

"Carol, don't go home. It just says Brownies because the rest of us were Brownies and they're expecting us to come. I wish I'd talked to some of the other kids." Carol was slowly turning away. "Carol, *please!*" It took a lot of persuasion, but finally Carol agreed to go in if Jenny would do the explaining.

Jenny opened the door. Carol followed, still somewhat reluctant. In front of them, on the floor, was a small rock with the letter 'A' on it. On top of the rock was a stone, and beside it a box full of pins. They each took a pin and looked around for a letter 'B'. Straight ahead, at the end of the short hall, they spotted it painted on a rock. It too had a stone on top, and another stone to its right. The box beside it held crayons. It took them longer to find the 'C'

because they looked down the left hallway first. When they found it, it was on a rock arranged with stones like the previous one. They took scissors from the box beside it and quickly found three more rock and stone arrangements with the letters 'D', 'E' and 'F', and boxes with papers in them. One paper had a list of the names of the Patrol Leaders in the Guide company. One had a copy of the Guide Promise, Law and Motto. The last paper simply said "You're almost there. Don't forget to eat part of the circle."

"I can hardly wait to see what we have to eat," said Jenny with excitement. "I never heard of eating a circle."

"Look," said Carol, her fears of being unwelcome gone, "on that big door. It's candy! I was expecting something yucky like — well, I don't know what — but not candy!"

Toffees wrapped in paper were taped to the door in a large circle. In the middle was a Guide hat. 'ENTER HERE' was written on a piece of masking tape across the hat. Behind them they could hear a couple of girls looking for the next letters on the alphabet trail. Carol and Jenny each took a candy and opened the door.

The hall was full of Guides, in various places, talking and laughing and doing things. Just inside the doorway at a table were three Guides who looked up at them smiling.

"Hi, you didn't get lost on the trail, eh? How did you like the end of it?"

"That was neat," said Jenny. "I really like toffee." She suddenly remembered Carol. "I brought my best friend. She wasn't a Brownie but I said she could come. It's O.K., isn't it? Do you think she can stay?"

"I'll ask Mrs. Mac." said one of the Guides.

Mrs. McKay came over and listened while Jenny tumbled out the story. "Of course, your friend can stay tonight. I think we have room for someone else anyhow. Some of the girls are fourteen and want to go to Rangers. They're just staying in Guides for a few weeks until the Rangers start meeting again. The Ranger leader just had a baby so the Ranger Advancement — that's when Guides go to Rangers officially — isn't until next month."

Jenny was jubilant. "Gee thanks, Mrs. McKay. I know I should've phoned and asked you. But I was scared you'd say no."

Carol looked very relieved. "Thank you," she said shyly.

"C'mon you guys," said one of the girls at the table. "Sorry, Mrs. Mac. I was really saying 'Guides', only the 'd' got lost in my toffee."

Mrs. Mac raised one eyebrow and laughed. "Well, they're not Guides yet, Debbie — but I'm sure they're not guys either. Jenny, you and Carol had better go and see what Deb wants you to do."

At the table they cut out the outlines of their feet. Each girl printed her first name on one footprint and pinned it to her blouse.

Debbie wrote their names on their other footprints and put them in a pile with others. "These belong to all the Guides," she explained. "We all came early and did that and some other stuff, like the trail."

Shortly after seven o'clock, when it seemed as if everyone had arrived, they all sat in a circle on the floor. There were six girls whom Jenny knew from Brownies. With everyone sitting on the floor, nobody looked too much taller than anyone else. Besides, almost everyone was either looking happy or chewing toffee. It was fun looking at the footprint name tags and seeing people's names. There wasn't another Jenny, but there was a Jennifer. That was Jenny's real name. Nobody ever called her that except her teachers at school before she asked them to call her Jenny, and her mother when she got mad at her.

"Welcome everyone," said Mrs. Mac. "I'm Mrs. McKay, your Guide Captain, and this is Mrs. Weston, our Lieutenant. It's really great to see all the girls who came up from Brownies here, and also Carol Green whom Jenny Evans brought. You all have a list of the Patrol Leaders. You can tell who they are because they have two white stripes on their left pockets.

"The Patrol Leaders — we usually call them P.L.'s for short — met last week and planned tonight's welcome meeting for you. I think each patrol got together and is going to introduce itself. Who's first? Alphabetical order?"

"Alphabetical order *backwards*. The Bluebirds *always* get stuck to go first!" said the Bluebird Patrol Leader.

Six girls stood up and made a line in the middle of the circle. The girl at one end crouched down, and the others got into positions of gradually increasing height, with the tallest girl at the opposite end, arms outstretched. Together they recited,

"Some of us Thistles are short,
Some of Thistles are tall,
But unless you step on us hard,
We're scarcely prickly at all.
                    Yea, Thistles!"

There were five members of the Robin Patrol. Each held up a card with a letter on it to spell out their patrol name. Then they sang a song about themselves to a vaguely recognizable tune.

"The Robins are cheerful, and tuneful, and early,
Our P.L. is Cathy and her hair's red and curly.
We like to go camping and talk all night long;
It's easier than rhyming so that's the end of
                    our song."

The next patrol had seven girls. The smallest one held up a large dark blue cardboard circle with nothing on it. The Patrol Leader held a similar one with a beautifully coloured stalk of fireweed on it. In turn, each girl spoke.

"When I became a Fireweed they told me I'd have to learn to embroider. I didn't even know what it meant!"

"That's because the Fireweed Patrol began eight years ago and the first Fireweed Patrol Leader was a girl who moved here from the Yukon."

She was very proud of the Yukon's flower, the fireweed, which is the first flower to grow again after an area has been burned out by a forest fire."

"Fireweed Patrol emblems cannot be bought, not even if you go to National Headquarters in Toronto."

"But you can buy blank patrol emblems and embroider them yourself. So the first Fireweed Patrol got blank emblems and a lady taught them to embroider."

"Unfortunately, every Fireweed always wants to keep her patrol emblem when she's finished with it, so new Fireweeds have to learn to embroider their own. Some kids even get their Needleworker Badge later because they like embroidery work."

"And some Guides — like me — vow they'll never pick up a needle again! But we're all glad we're Fireweeds."

The Daffodil Patrol got up, looking a little bit abashed. One of them said, "We're the Daffodils and we're not very original or historic, but we sure have loud voices. So, give me a 'D'!" By the time they had spelled out Daffodil (with three 'f's) the room was echoing with the sound of their enthusiastic yell.

The Bluebirds all stood up. "We want you new guys to help us. We're going to say something and then you all shout 'hurray'. The next thing we say, shout 'boo' and then 'hurray', and then 'boo', and the last time the loudest 'hurray' you can. Got it?" Everyone nodded. "O.K. Bluebirds, let's go!"

"Bluebirds are beautiful!" The 'hurray' could scarcely be heard amid the general laughter.

"Bluebirds go south in winter." A faint 'boo' came back.

"Bluebirds make everybody who sees them happy." A strong 'hurray' followed.

"Bluebirds are rare these days." "Boo!"

"Bluebirds are us and we've got room for more!" "Hurray!"

Mrs. Weston said, "And you were the bunch who didn't have any ideas! I think you've all done a good job of telling the new girls something about your patrols, don't you, Mrs. Mac?"

"I certainly do," agreed Mrs. Mac. "With seven new girls we might have to create another patrol, but we'll see how things go. You can take a couple of weeks to decide which patrol you think you'd like to belong to. Sometimes we do things all together as a company; sometimes the patrols do things together as patrols; and often we're doing things in different kinds of groups, or even alone. It all depends what you want to do and how best we can work it in. But right now, some of the girls have to do something with all these footprints. Mrs. Weston would like the rest of you to go outside with her while it's still light enough to see."

Jenny and Carol put on their jackets and joined the chattering group on the lawn behind the church. Mrs. Weston held up her hand. Jenny whispered to Carol, "Hold your hand up, Carol. That means 'Freeze' and we're not supposed to talk or move or anything." In a few seconds, every girl had one arm raised and all was perfectly still.

"Before we go home tonight we're going to have a campfire and sing some songs, and then roast marshmallows. We aren't usually allowed to light fires in town, but the Fire Chief said we could tonight as long as we're very careful. And we thought we might as well do a good turn for the church caretaker while we're at it.

"I'm going to divide you into three groups, about nine in each group — so find a buddy if you want to be with someone especially. Each group will have a plastic bag. The first group will make a line, about arm's length apart, and go back and forth across the lawn and the parking lot and pick up any pieces of paper. The second group will do the same, only you'll pick up all the garbage that isn't paper. The third group will take their bag near all the trees and the hedge, especially at the front of the building, and look for dead wood on the ground. Dead wood that is still on the tree burns better than wood that's on the ground which might be damp or rotten. But don't break off dead branches if it's going to leave an ugly spot. Make sure it's dead! Dead wood should snap and not just bend when you try to break it. So be careful. Has anyone any questions?"

"How do we know when we're done?" asked one girl.

"Either when your bag is full or you can't find any more."

"Suppose our bag is full and there's still more stuff to get?"

"Well, come back and check with me. I'll be at the back end of the parking lot where we're going to lay the fire. Are you all straight now? See if you can get yourselves into three groups of nine."

Carol and Jenny joined the group that was given the bag in which to gather firewood. The Daffodil Patrol Leader was in the same group. Her name was Heather and she seemed to be a lot of fun. She gathered the group around her.

"We'll need different sizes of wood," she said. "Mostly a lot of really skinny sticks. We'll use the paper garbage that the other group is finding to start the fire, but then we'll need a big pile of sticks no bigger around than a pencil, for kindling. The paper might be dampish so it would be a good idea to look for some tinder too."

"There's some dead Queen Anne's lace among the live flowers

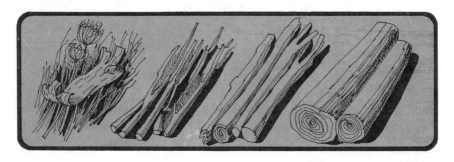

at the edge of the parking lot," said a girl named Jan. "It's really good tinder."

"Right," replied Heather. "Just don't get any leaves. They make so much smoke that the Fire Chief might come roaring up. See that horse chestnut tree? Forget it. We had an awful time once on a hike. We thought we were being smart and took a bunch of dead twigs from it with us. It's got good conkers, but it sure doesn't burn well."

"There's that big old oak tree at the side of the hall. Maybe there will be some dead sticks under it. It really burns. My dad says oak holds the heat better than almost anything."

"Yeah, and I noticed a Christmas tree — well, I mean a spruce or a pine or something. That's what we use for kindling in our fireplace at the cottage."

It wasn't hard to find dead sticks around the trees. Heather said she wanted skinny sticks. The first ones that Carol picked up looked very thin, but when she took a pencil out of her pocket and measured them beside it she found they were four times as thick. Then she found a branch under a maple tree. It looked as if it had come down in last week's windstorm. It had lots of twigs on it that were even thinner than her pencil. When she held both ends and bent it, it snapped with a crisp sound.

"Listen," said Jenny. "I hear a whistle from behind the church." Five short blasts of a whistle sounded clearly.

"Come on, you guys," shouted Heather. "That's the 'everybody-come-come-quickly' whistle. It means we're wanted. Our bag is about full anyhow. We've got enough to cook a dinner, not just marshmallows! Oh well, better too much than not enough. That's disaster! Once you've started the fire, nobody ever wants to leave and go to find more wood."

The three groups gathered around Mrs. Weston in the parking lot.

"It didn't take you long to fill those bags! I wouldn't have dreamed there was that much garbage and paper around. The place *looked* pretty clean to me at the beginning."

"It shows what you can find when you're observant. It comes from all those Kim's games we play," said a girl with dark sparkling eyes.

"What's Kim's game?" asked one of the new girls.

"It's a neat game. Mrs. Weston, can we play a super Kim's game next week instead of telling them about it now?"

"Sure, Moira. Only you can't keep the garbage to use for it!"

"Yuck!" said Moira, turning up her nose. "I'd like an elegant Kim's game."

"That might be a tall order. Can you think one up?"

"I don't know. But I'd rather play. If I make it up, I can't play it, and I have this little thing going with myself. I'm aiming for 100 per cent perfection, total recall. I don't think I'll ever make it — but anyhow, I'm a good garbage-finder. Anti-pollution, that's me."

Mrs. Weston asked Heather and another girl to show the rest how to lay the fire. Carol had never heard of laying a fire before. She thought you just put a pile of sticks down and lit them with a match. She watched carefully. First they made a circle of stones. Mrs. Weston said it wasn't really necessary on a gravel parking lot, but it would help them keep the fire small which was much safer. She said the Indians used to laugh at the white man who usually made great roaring fires to cook a small dinner, thereby making far more mess and using far more wood than was necessary. Heather crumpled up a couple of handfuls of paper, put the dead weeds, broken up, on top of that, and then some short thin sticks. She laid them this way and that, explaining that you always had to leave air spaces because fire needs oxygen to burn.

"I'm going to make a log-cabin fire. It'll last well."

It was easy to see why she called it a log-cabin fire. Around the pile of tinder and kindling, arranged in a pyramid shape, Heather and Alison laid longer and thicker sticks in a crisscross fashion in

much the same way that a log cabin was built. They added more sticks to the inner part.

"There. That should be good. I left a twisted bit of paper sticking out at the bottom so that I have something that will light from a match. We've got some of those firelighters we made. They're inside in our patrol box. You know, the ones we made by cutting old waxed milk cartons and TV dinner containers into long strips. They're just like having an extra-long match, except you have to light them from a real match first. We'll leave the extra wood in the bag."

"That looks great," said Mrs. Weston.

"Don't you think we should cover the fire in case it rains or gets dewy?" asked Alison. "We can stuff the extra paper in the bag with the other garbage in it and then use the empty bag to cover the fire, until we're ready to light it. It'll stay down if we put heavy stones at the corners."

This done, they took the garbage inside with them and went to see what Mrs. Mac and the six girls with her had been preparing. As soon as they entered the hall, they noticed the floor covered with red footprints. Mrs. Mac asked everyone to remove one shoe and look for the footprint they thought was their own, without looking at the name on the back. For a few minutes it was wildly chaotic. Then gradually, as girls found the prints that matched their feet and sat down beside them, it became easier for Jenny and Carol to identify theirs.

Carol had a small disagreement with a girl whose feet were just about the same size, but Carol recognized her little toe which curled in a lot. When all had matched their feet to their footprints, they sat in a large circle again. Mrs. Mac asked them if they'd had any trouble drawing their feet with the hand they didn't usually use. Almost everyone had, especially the right-handers.

"That's interesting," she commented. "I wonder why those who are left-handed had less trouble. Did you know that Lord Baden-Powell, who founded Guides and Scouts, could use both hands equally well? That's called being ambidextrous. They tell the story about him practising the piano when he was a schoolboy. He had been teased about trying to do things with both hands because some of the boys thought he was showing off. He replied he might need to use his left hand if he ever injured or lost his right. "Suppose you got both hands cut off, what would you do then?" one of the boys had asked scornfully. That was just the kind of challenge Baden-Powell loved. He rigged up the piano bench in the music room so that he could sit on it and use his feet to reach the piano keyboard. One day, a teacher passing the music room heard a tune he thought he recognized being played on the piano, but there was something very strange about the painfully slow manner of playing. When he looked in the room, he was as-tounded to see the young B-P (that was Baden-Powell's nick-name) tied to the piano bench, his arms behind him, attempting to play the National Anthem with his bare toes. Try it sometime!

"Baden-Powell could not only use both hands equally well, but he could draw two different things at the same time. He said it saved time! That's a real challenge for me. Whenever I try drawing a house with one hand and a tree with the other, I usually end up with two tree-houses!

"That's why we asked you to draw your feet with the other hand. Did any of you try doing it in the dark?"

Almost everyone had, and some had even found it easier, just as Carol and Jenny had. Nobody could figure that out.

"What we want you to do now," continued Mrs. Mac, "is to turn you footprints over — I see some of you have already discovered there's something written on the other side — and you'll see that we've written one of the Guide laws on it. Most of the laws are written on three different footprints, a couple on four. Go around and find who has the same law you have. Then find a spot to sit with your little group. Get far enough away from the other groups so that you won't bother each other. Talk about what the law means and then plan a very short skit about it. We'll do the skits next week, but you have about fifteen minutes now to plan before it's time to go out for campfire. The skit should take no longer than three minutes to perform. You may have a little time next week to polish it up. If you need any help, Mrs. Weston and I will be free as soon as we gather up some of our papers here."

Carol's footprint read 'A Guide smiles and sings even under difficulty'. She soon found the other two girls to make up a group. One was Cathy, the red-headed leader of the Robin Patrol.

Jenny had 'A Guide is thrifty' written on her footprint. She didn't have the least idea what it meant and was glad hers turned out to be one of the four-people groups. Her father always said that two heads were better than one unless they were on the same body. Four should be twice as good.

Jenny's group had another new girl in it. She thought 'thrifty' meant being speedy. The other two Guides explained that wasn't it at all. It meant not being wasteful but using whatever you had in the best possible way.

"You know," said a girl named Liz, "like not wasting food by leaving it on your plate, or throwing away what you don't finish at a meal. My mum makes super casseroles. She collects all the leftovers — not from our plates, but you know what I mean — and puts them in the freezer. The day before my dad's payday we almost always have one of her Casserole Treasures that she makes with all sorts of leftovers and a can of mushroom soup. I hate mushrooms, but I sure like our Casserole Treasures."

"It's not just food," said the other Guide, "or even things. It's time, too. If you don't waste your time doing nothing or just fooling around all the time, you've got time to do what you're supposed to do and all the neat things you want to do. The girl next door to me never does anything. You should see her. She spends all her time trying to make up her mind, or complaining that there's nothing to do. That's *really* wasteful."

"I think I know what you mean," said Jenny. "It would be money, too, wouldn't it? Last week I blew three weeks' allowance on a dumb game at the carnival at the booth where you throw rings on stuffed animals. I was sure I'd get one on — it looked so easy — but I never did. My brother said I was a sucker. I didn't believe him, but I do now. I had to miss all the rides because I didn't have any money left. Was I ever mad!"

"And then, there's the big things, like Canada's water supply," said Liz, "and trees and oil and stuff like that. We were talking about it in school and the teacher said if we use up all our natural resources as fast as we have been doing, there might not be any left by the time we're old."

"Yeah, but that's not for a long time. I'm only ten."

"That's just the point. You have to plan ahead in order to be really thrifty. Let's start making up our skit now. We could be a bunch of rich kids who . . ." and the plans got underway.

It seemed no time at all before Mrs. Mac raised her hand and everyone froze — not quite as fast as they had outside, because it was hard to stop talking about your skit when you'd just begun.

"The Patrol Seconds are looking after the campfire tonight," said Mrs. Weston. "I'll go out with them now and make sure everything's ready to start. We'll take all the sit-upons out with us, and the marshmallows, and sticks I cut earlier at home. Give us five minutes to get ready, will you Mrs. Mac, and then the rest of you come out?"

When the rest of the Guide company went outside it was dark. A great orange moon hung in the sky and the air was edged with an autumnal chill. You couldn't see any stars at first until your eyes got used to the dark. Then Jenny saw the first star.

"Star light, star bright, first star I've
seen tonight, I wish I may, I wish I might,
have the wish I wish tonight."

"What did you wish, Jenny?" asked Carol, knowing she'd never tell lest it spoil the wish.

"You know, Carol; I bet you're wishing the same thing," and she hoped that Carol too was wishing Guides would always be as much fun.

When the girls were sitting on the waterproof squares, and everyone was very quiet, a bird called softly in the stillness of the evening. Suddenly a cat miaowed and hissed. Jenny grabbed Carol's sleeve and whispered, "Sit closer, it's kinda spooky here in the dark. But isn't it neat? It makes me feel shivery."

Heather's Second lit a match to her firelighter. Then she held it carefully under the twist of paper which had been left poking out from the bottom of the laid fire. A flame crackled upward. It jumped from stick to stick and the Queen Anne's lace tops were soon gone, but they left enough heat to ignite the small sticks above them. A voice spoke, slowly and solemnly, "May our new friends who have come tonight find our friendship as warm as this fire and as lasting as the forests from which the trees come."

Jenny knew a few of the songs they sang from Brownies. Some of the others were easy to catch on to, like the one that was full of tra-la-las and cuckoos. The one she liked best was near the end, sung in parts, and it sent tingles down her spine. Then they all stood up while Heather spoke.

"St. Francis lived hundreds of years ago in Italy and became very poor so that he could serve God and his fellow man. He could talk to the birds and the animals and they all knew and loved him. This is part of a prayer of his that says what we probably all would like to say to God.

'O Lord, make me an instrument of your peace;
where there is hatred, let me sow love;
where there is injury, pardon; where there
is discord, union; where there is doubt,
faith; where there is despair, hope; where
there is darkness, light; and where there
is sadness, joy. Amen.'

Looking into the fire, with its embers glowing, they sang 'Taps'. Mrs. Mac broke the silence which followed.

"It's time for marshmallows and other good things. I hope you'll all be back next week and that you will want to be Guides."

Want to be Guides! Jenny knew that was what she wanted to be. There was no doubt in her mind now. She looked at Carol. "I'm coming back, Jenny," Carol said. "I wouldn't miss it for the world."

Roasting the marshmallows was fun. There were graham wafers and milk chocolate bars too. Everyone put a roasted marshmallow between two wafers and popped in a piece of chocolate.

"These are yummy!" said Carol.

"That's why they're called 'Some Mores', because you always want some more," said Heather. "Something else that's good is Marshmalluck. We invented it when I did my Camp Leader Badge. You take a raw marshmallow — like this — and keep pulling it out, rolling it up into a ball, pulling it out again, over and over, and it turns into Marshmalluck."

Cars started entering the parking lot.

"There's your mum, Jenny," said Carol. "I guess we have to go. We'd better see if it's all right to leave now."

On the way home, Mrs. Evans listened to the girls' chatter.

"It sounds as if you had a good time!"

"We sure did," said Jenny. "Mum, do we have any marshmallows at home, and graham wafers and chocolate bars?"

"Marshmallows maybe, but that's all, I think."

"Oh well," sighed Carol. "You can always try Marshmalluck."

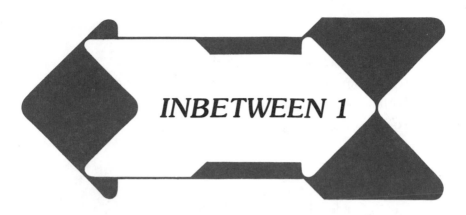

INBETWEEN 1

All over the world, wherever there are Girl Guides or Girl Scouts, they make a three-fold Promise and have a Guide Law. No matter what language these are in, they include the same ideas: duty to God and country; helping others; obeying the Guide Law. They vary in wording but not in meaning from country to country. Every Guide or Girl Scout wears a pin or badge that either *is* a trefoil, or includes a trefoil — three leaves, to remind her of her three-fold Promise.

Guide Promise

I promise, on my honour, to do my best:
To do my duty to God, the Queen and my country,
To help other people at all times,
To obey the Guide Law.

Guide Law

1. A Guide's honour is to be trusted.
2. A Guide is loyal.
3. A Guide is useful and helps others.
4. A Guide is a friend to all and a sister to every Guide.
5. A Guide is courteous.
6. A Guide is kind to animals and enjoys the beauty in nature.
7. A Guide is obedient.
8. A Guide smiles and sings even under difficulty.
9. A Guide is thrifty.
10. A Guide is pure in thought, word and deed.

Every Guide should know the Promise and Law by heart, but even more important is knowing what they mean and wanting to live up to them. As you grow older, you will find that their meaning deepens. None of the laws is easy to keep. What matters is that *you* try *your* best.

BE PREPARED

When Lord Baden-Powell, the Founder of Scouting and Guiding, chose these words as the Boy Scout and Girl Guide Motto, he knew that the best way to be of use to oneself and to other people was by being prepared for almost anything that could happen. Thus Guides have always liked to learn all sorts of new skills and try things out for themselves.

Put a check mark (✔) beside the things you already know how to do.

Put a star (*) beside the things you would like to learn how to do.

Simple first aid
How to lay and light a fire with wood
How to start a charcoal fire without a liquid fire starter
How to bake and ice a birthday cake
A safe way to rescue someone who has fallen through the ice on a river
How to do mouth-to-mouth resuscitation
How to make a telephone call to report a fire
Three ways to amuse a small child
How to catch and clean a fish
How to cook a simple meal
How to find north with a compass
How to find north without a compass
How to recognize the poison ivy plant
How to use a screwdriver properly
How to sing a song in another language
How to operate some kind of boat

There are many, many ways in which you can be prepared to help, both in an emergency of some sort, and in ordinary, everyday things. Try making a list of things you know how to do that aren't on the list above and share it with another Guide.

LAYING AND FOLLOWING TRAILS

When the North American Indian wanted to lay a trail to let his companions know which way he had gone, he used the natural materials he found at hand: sticks, rocks, stones, grass, trees. In the woods, he made a slash with his hatchet on a tree or bent a young sapling to the ground to indicate the direction he had taken. This is something you wouldn't do today, when many of our forests in the southern part of Canada are gone and we wish to preserve the remaining trees for the many people who now live in Canada.

The other means used by the Indians are fun to try. Make sure your signs are not too far apart: the second sign should be within sight of the first. Whatever direction your sign says you have taken, make sure you go that way without walking in a curve. Look back and "sight" along your arm to the previous sign as a means of checking your accuracy. Whenever you change direc-

TRAIL SIGNS

STRAIGHT AHEAD	TURN RIGHT	TURN LEFT	DO NOT GO THIS WAY
Rocks			
Pebbles			
Sticks			
Long Grass			
[5]	Number of Paces in Direction Indicated		I have gone home

tion, you need a sign. The sign indicating the end of the trail is like a diagram representing an Indian in his teepee (looking down on it), and means 'I have gone home'. This sign is engraved on Lord Baden-Powell's gravestone to show that he has 'gone home' to God.

OTHER KINDS OF TRAILS

There are many hiking trails in Canada and the U.S.A. which you can follow. These go over all kinds of different terrain and generally use painted trail signs, often a vertical rectangle, about 20 cm. x 5 cm., on trees, rocks, posts or other obvious surfaces. A double rectangle indicates a turn.

You are familiar with informal trails made simply by people walking in the same place, over and over, thereby wearing down the grass to make a path. Most of our highways had their beginnings in this way in pioneer days. Even when a path is not well-worn, you can spot where people have gone before you by looking for such signs as broken branches, footprints, and unfortunately these days, pop bottles and candy wrappers.

There are other ways of laying trails for outdoor games. Tie bits of coloured wool to trees, or sprinkle oatmeal occasionally, or give compass directions, or give landmark directions.

Trail games are fun if occasionally along the trail there are directions to do something, observe something, find a 'treasure', or rescue a 'victim'.

HAND AND WHISTLE SIGNALS

If everyone can see you, it is more effective (and easier on the ears) to use hand signals. All signals should be obeyed promptly.

hand straight up overhead — freeze, stop, silence

hand moved quickly up and down several times — everyone come quickly, rally, fall in

hand held high and waved slowly from side to side — scatter, go out

hand waved horizontally from side to side across the face — no, never mind, as you were

hands describing circle — form circle

hands stretched out — form two lines

hands describing U — form semi-circle

When the others can't see you, use a whistle to give directions. Make sure you blow the whistle sharply and clearly distinguish between the short and long blasts.

_____ means a long blast   _ _ _ _ scatter, go out

•   means a short blast   ••• ___ Patrol Leaders
                                       come here

_____ freeze, stop, silence   •_•_•_ alarm! look out

•••• everyone come quickly,
     fall in, rally

TRY THESE GAMES

Bean Bag Snatch

Formation: Players are in two lines facing each other, some distance apart. A bean bag is in the middle, between the lines. The players are numbered from opposite ends.

To Play: The game leader calls a number, and the girl from each line with that number tries to snatch the bean bag and return to her own place without being tagged by the other player. Two numbers can be called, and tagging be done only by the player with the same number as the one who got the bean bag.

Thunder and Lightning

Formation: Players sitting on floor in a circle. Two bean bags are needed. The bean bags are the thunder.

To Play: Starting from opposite sides of the circle, the bean bags are passed, one clockwise and the other counter-clockwise, around the circle without being thrown or dropped. When the game leader blows the whistle (which is 'lightning'), the two players holding the bean bags, must turn their backs and can no longer play. When players can no longer reach each other, they make a smaller, inner circle and the others can turn and watch. The last two left in win.

Stalking the Hat

Formation: Players seated on floor in as large a circle as possible. One player, blindfolded, is in the centre. A hat is behind the centre player and a few feet away is a ruler or a thin stick.

To Play: Game leader chooses one person who creeps silently and picks up the stick. She then attempts to lift the hat with the stick and carry it on the stick back to her place. If the blindfolded player hears her, she points in the direction of the sound. If she points straight at the stalker, a new stalker is selected after the hat and stick are replaced. A successful stalker may become the next blind-folded person.

Instead of pointing, it is more fun to use a squirt-gun and have the blindfolded person squirt water in the direction of the sound. Or, in a darkened room, use a flashlight and catch the stalker in the beam.

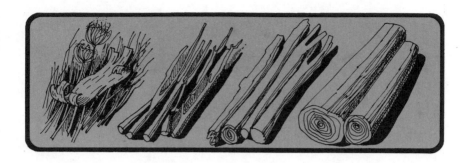

FUEL FOR THE FIRE

First you need tinder. Crumpled paper can be used, but a Guide likes to be able to make a fire using only natural materials. Whatever tinder you use it *must* be dry. The tinder goes on the bottom and it's what you light with your match. If a match won't light it, it's not good tinder.

Try: birch bark (not torn from a living tree); dead weed stalks and tops that snap when you bend them; very thin twigs from a softwood tree — no thicker than a match, but longer; shavings from softwood; fuzz stick whittled from dry softwood.

Next you need kindling. This is wood which burns easily and quickly and which will catch fire from the burning tinder. Kindling is thin and dry. "Take the dead from the living" is good advice when looking for kindling. Small dead branches on the lower parts of trees are often available.

Try: pine, cedar, tamarack, birch, aspen, soft maple, fir.

Last you need firewood. This is the slow-burning, long-lasting wood which gives you a good steady heat and hot coals for baking.

Try: hickory, beech, oak, maple, hornbeam, apple, birch, ash.

Avoid if possible trees that don't burn well, like willow, elm, horse chestnut.

Putting Out the Fire

Always when you light a fire, make sure you have something nearby, for example, water or sand to extinguish it. Pour water or sand gently on the fire. Stir with a stick. Continue until the fire place feels cold to your touch. Turn partly burned wood over to make sure it is out.

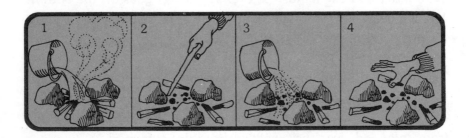

Home Made Fire Starters

From a woodworking shop, gather sawdust. Place it in a card-board (not plastic foam) egg carton. Fill carefully with melted wax, putting a bit of string in the centre as a wick to light. (When melting paraffin or candle stubs, always use a double boiler, or use a can set in a pan of hot water. *Never* melt wax over direct heat since it can burst into flames very easily.)

Save small candle stubs. Wrap them in several layers of waxed paper and twist the ends.

Roll newspaper into tight rolls. Tie with string every few inches. Dip into melted wax until saturated. Cut into individual starters.

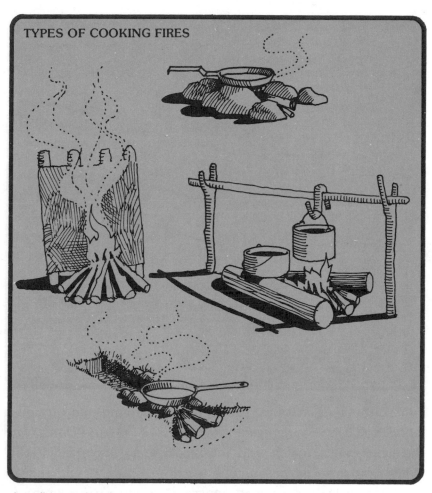

TYPES OF COOKING FIRES

A reflector fire has a back which reflects heat onto what you are cooking. Try aluminum foil wrapped around upright stakes made of green wood or metal.

Dig a rectangular trench or pit in which to build a trench fire. Lay a rack across it for your pots. Replace the earth and sod carefully when you are finished. Place rocks (or logs, although this can be wasteful) so that a grate, rack or pot can be supported on them. This is often called a Hunter Fire.

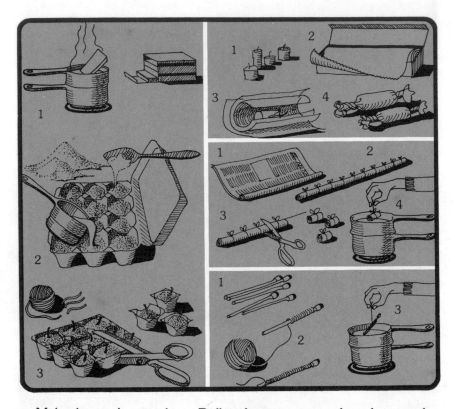

Make hunter's matches. Roll soft string around and around a wooden match, securing with a half hitch at the end. Don't wrap the head of the match. Dip the whole thing into melted wax. When you strike it, the hunter's match will burn slowly and for much longer than an ordinary match. *They are also waterproof.*

Using Charcoal

Charcoal can be started from tinder just like a wood fire, or you can use homemade fire starters. Make a little pile of charcoal and poke two or three fire starters into it. When they are burning well, the charcoal will gradually ignite. Charcoal is ready to use when most of the black has disappeared and glows white.

Make a Charcoal Buddy Burner

You will need a large, clean juice can. Remove one end. With a pair of tinsnips, cut a door as illustrated. Punch holes around the top. To use the buddy burner with charcoal, set it on an old baking pan or several thicknesses of foil. Place a charcoal lighter (do not use a liquid starter) and a pile of charcoal in the can. Ignite the starter. Within twenty minutes or so, the charcoal should be glowing with a white heat. The top of the can will be very hot and ready to cook on. This sort of burner can also be used with wood. Make sure you have lots of small, dry pieces on hand, because it will need replenishing often.

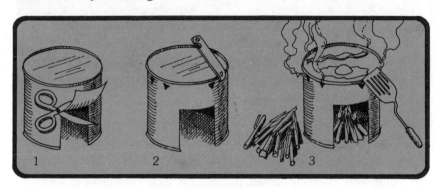

SOME MORES SOUND GOOD?
HERE ARE SOME MORE SIMPLE RECIPES
TO COOK ON AN OPEN FIRE

Banana Dream Boats

You will need: one banana, 12 chocolate chips or a small milk chocolate bar, about 10 miniature marshmallows, aluminum foil

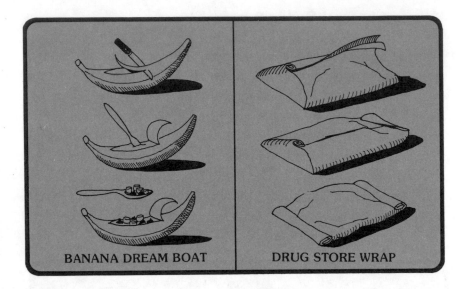

| BANANA DREAM BOAT | DRUG STORE WRAP |

To make: With a knife, cut a flap on the side of the banana, leaving the flap attached at one end. Scoop out about ½″ of banana (eat), and fill the cavity thus made, with the chocolate and marshmallows. Close the flap. Wrap the banana in foil using drugstore wrap method.

Bake in hot coals of fire about 5 or 10 minutes. Some like the chocolate and marshmallows barely melted, others like them all squishy. It's up to you.

TIPS WHEN USING ALUMINUM FOIL WRAP

1. Use the drugstore wrap method as illustrated.
2. Wrap the food in the foil with the shiny side IN.
3. To prevent food from burning, wrap it in foil, then in wet newspaper or paper towelling, then again in foil.
4. Make sure your foil packets are in the hot part of your fire, after the flames have died down. Turn them and move them occasionally.

Super Baked Apples

You will need: one apple, handful of butterscotch chips, handful of miniature marshmallows, aluminum foil

To make: Remove the core of the apple carefully. Set the apple on a square of foil. Fill the cavity with butterscotch chips and marshmallows. Wrap the apple in foil.
Bake in hot coals of fire until apple is soft. This depends on the kind of apple and heat of fire — anywhere from 10 to 30 minutes. You can use traditional baked apple fillings like brown sugar and raisins but you'll find this one especially delicious.

Grilled Cheese Sandwich

You will need: one cheese slice, two slices of bread, margarine, aluminum foil

To make: Place a cheese slice between two slices of bread and spread margarine on the *outside* of both slices. Wrap in foil. Bake in hot coals of fire, for about two minutes, then turn and bake for another two minutes. Check to see if bread is browned. Your fire may not have been hot enough and it may take longer. You can also grill cheese sandwiches in a frying pan or on the grate.

Steakette Dinner

You will need: one steakette, raw potatoes sliced thinly, or canned potatoes, about 1/4 package of dried onion soup mix, aluminum foil

To make: Place steakette on foil (double thickness is best), spread potato slices on top, then sprinkle with dried soup mix. Seal package and bake in hot coals, turning occasionally, for about 15 minutes.

Jenny and Carol were sitting around a table with the Daffodil Patrol on their second night at Guides. Suddenly the door was flung open and a woman burst into the room, shouting. She was wearing a fur jacket and the handbag over her arm was bulging.

Mrs. McKay and Mrs. Weston hurried over to her. Every patrol corner in the room was hushed and every girl watched intently. The woman's shouts sank to a whisper, punctuated by sobs. The girls strained to hear what was being said.

"I'll phone the police right away," said Mrs. Weston clearly and she started to go towards the telephone.

"No! Not that!" screamed the woman, and as abruptly as she had arrived, she turned and ran from the room. Mrs. Weston hurried after the woman, and shut the door behind her.

Mrs. McKay signalled the patrols to make a circle on the floor so that she could speak to them. Her voice quivered slightly, but Jenny thought she looked very brave and calm. She hoped Mrs. Weston had caught up with the poor woman.

"Girls, I was so busy trying to hear what that woman was trying to tell me, that I really didn't get a good look at her. Did any of you?"

"Yes." "I sure did." "What was the matter with her?" A clamour of voices answered.

"I'm not too sure. But just in case Mrs. Weston doesn't catch up with her, it would be a good idea if we had a description of her so that we can tell the police if necessary. Would each patrol write down everything they can remember about her?"

The patrols grouped together. Carol thought she would never forget how frightened the woman had looked. She could see her now, short blonde hair all over her head as if she had been running in the wind, a bright red scarf showing above the collar of the brown fur jacket — was it mink? Carol wasn't sure — brown checked slacks and running shoes. She was sure she was wearing white running shoes.

"No, she wasn't," said one of the girls adamantly. "She had on brown leather shoes." They all argued about it until it seemed as if the woman must have had fourteen feet to wear all the different shoes the girls thought they saw. One thing they were all agreed on was that the handbag must have bulged with money; it was that kind of bulge.

When Mrs. McKay asked each Patrol Leader to read out her patrol's description of the woman, they found they all agreed on some things, like the colour of her hair and the kind of handbag she carried. Some patrols were sure she wore glasses. Three patrols said with great certainty that she had white running shoes. That made Carol feel good.

The door opened again, and in walked Mrs. Weston with the woman. They were both smiling. The woman took off her glasses — and her hair! It was a wig!

"Mrs. Mac! That was a mean trick!" exclaimed Moira. "I should have guessed. That fur coat — and I was the one who asked Mrs. Weston if we could play an elegant Kim's Game! How could I be so dumb? I wasn't even suspicious!"

Mrs. McKay shook her head and smiled, "I didn't think we'd fool you, Moira. It was Mrs. Weston's idea that we do it this way. Her neighbour, Joan, was home from college and figured she could put on a good enough disguise to fool even those of you who know her. Joan, how would you like to pose for everyone and describe what you were wearing? Do it slowly enough that the patrols can check their lists and see how observant they were."

Most of the patrols had reasonably good descriptions. Two had even put 'wig?' down. The Fireweed Patrol had written at the bottom that it could be somebody in disguise. When Mrs. McKay asked what was in her handbag to make such a bulge, Joan opened it to reveal a huge wad of facial tissues. So much for the hundred dollar bills envisaged by the Daffodils.

"That's Kim's Game," said Mrs. Weston. "There are ever so many ways you can play it. It's a way to improve your observation skills, something that's very useful in life. This particular game shows you how many people can see the same thing at the same time and yet think they saw all sorts of different things. If you really had to give a description to the police, say if a crime were committed (and I'm sure many of you thought a crime had been committed when Joan burst in) or an accident had happened, could you do it accurately? It takes practice, and that's why we often play Kim's Game."

One of the new girls asked, "Why is it called Kim's Game? That's my name."

"There's a book by Rudyard Kipling called *Kim*. It's about Kimball O'Hara, an Irish orphan in India in the last century who was trained by an old jeweller to be a sort of detective or spy. The old man used to put many kinds of jewels on a tray and give Kim a minute to observe them. Then he'd cover the tray and ask Kim to describe the jewels. At first Kim had trouble, but with practice he became very good at remembering all kinds of minor details about the jewels. This made him a very clever detective. Lord Baden-Powell — who had done a bit of spy work when he was in the army — was impressed by this method of training the senses. That means *all* your senses, because you should be able to identify and remember sounds and smells and how things feel, as well as how they look. Scouts and Guides have always played Kim's Game."

"My aunt once saw a hit-and-run accident when she was driving," said Moira. "She wrote the license number in the dust on the dashboard (she was lucky it was dusty). One of the numbers wasn't very clear, but she had memorized everything she could about the car, and they caught the man."

Mrs. McKay turned to Joan, who had removed the fur jacket and wig. "Joan, before you go, will you tell the Guides what you're doing at college?"

"Sure. I'm in a Forestry course, and it's really interesting. There are ten girls and sixty-four boys — that makes it even more interesting." Everyone laughed. "Actually, they haven't had girls in the course for very long, and some of the boys still aren't convinced it's the place for them. But most of them are pretty good about it. Last week we had a party at somebody's cottage, and the guys started kidding the girls about not being strong enough to cut down a tree — the weaker sex and all that! A few of the girls really didn't know anything about it (we don't do it in the course), but some of us had been Guides and Rangers, and one girl had lived in the bush up north most of her life. What she doesn't know about using an axe isn't worth knowing. She's short, but wow! The owner of the cottage had a tree that had to come down, and we brought it down, precisely where we wanted it. The guys were impressed, believe me. The next day one of them asked to see the blisters on my hand and was disappointed when there weren't any. I didn't tell him I'd spent most of the summer paddling a canoe."

Before she left, Joan promised to come back sometime when she was home and help anyone who wanted to work on her Woodman Badge. "Or Fisherman," she added. "This term we do a lot of stuff on fish. Maybe we could go ice fishing in the winter on the lake."

After she left, Mrs. McKay got the new girls (she called them recruits) together around a table.

"The others are having special Patrol in Council meetings to decide what they want to do for the next month. They'll all write down what activities they want to do, any badges they want to work on and so forth — any ideas at all. Then the Patrol Leaders and Seconds have a meeting called the Court of Honour. There we discuss all the ideas and try to figure out how we can work it all in. We can't always do everything, but we try."

"How come we can't do that, too?" asked Nancy. She had been in Jenny's Six in Brownies.

"You could, except none of you has decided which patrol you want to be in yet. Besides, at the last Court of Honour, they decided that it might be better if you saw how the Guide company operated for a month. They wanted me to tell you tonight about the Tenderfoot Test — the things you have to do before you can be enrolled as a Guide. We don't always do it like this. Sometimes, we've put recruits into patrols on their first night, but the Court of Honour voted to let you choose your patrol after you know us a bit better."

"Suppose we all want to go in the same patrol?" asked Nancy.

"They thought of that, too! They said we'd have to draw names in that case, unless some of you had second, or even third, choices. I really think it will work out all right. The patrols are different and they're all pretty nice."

"Several years ago the Court of Honour decided that no patrol should be larger than eight, but most of the girls prefer five or six. They say it's easier to get along that way. It's one of the things we vote about every year. Another is whether we'll have an election for new Patrol Leaders."

"What happens when you vote?" asked Jenny. "Does everyone get to vote?"

"Most of the time only the Court of Honour votes and the

Patrol Leaders are trusted to vote the way their patrol has decided. But for some things, like for new Patrol Leaders, the whole company votes by secret ballot. If only one patrol needs a new P.L. — when somebody moves or goes to Rangers or wants to resign as P.L. — then that patrol usually votes for its own."

"What does secret ballot mean?"

"I know," said Carol. "We did it at school once. It's when everyone writes what she wants on a paper so that nobody else can see, and the teacher or somebody who didn't vote counts the paper to find out who or what won. We were voting on what to eat at the class picnic."

"But last week I was with the group of kids talking about the Guide law that says a Guide's honour is to be trusted. Having your vote secret sounds as if you don't trust somebody," protested Nancy.

"That's an interesting point, Nancy," said Mrs. McKay. "What do the rest of you think?"

Everyone sat quietly for a moment, and then Carol spoke. "Well, if I had to vote for a Patrol Leader and my best friend, like Jenny, wanted to be Patrol Leader and I knew she wanted to, and I didn't think she'd be the best Patrol Leader even if she was my best friend, I'd rather she didn't know I'd voted for somebody else."

"That's mean, Carol!" cried Jenny. She felt funny inside to hear Carol say that. "I don't think that would make you a very good friend. I would be trusting you to vote for me, and I wouldn't even know how you voted if it was a secret." For the first time she felt like fighting with Carol. It was hard to keep back the tears.

Mrs. McKay could see the struggle Jenny was having. She knew that Carol was wishing she hadn't said what she did. The dismay showed on Carol's face as she realized that her words had hurt Jenny. Mrs. McKay's voice was gentle.

"I think Carol's trying to say that a secret ballot makes it easier

for a person to vote the way she thinks she should, even if it might
hurt someone she likes a lot if that person knew how she voted.
She wouldn't want to hurt a friend, but she might honestly believe
the friend wasn't the best person for the job. If the voting were
done by a show of hands, she might feel she *had* to vote for her
friend in order not to hurt her. And Jenny, it's a little early to be
worried about who's going to vote for you to be Patrol Leader!"

"I just like to be prepared," said Jenny in self-defence. She was
feeling a little foolish.

"Anyhow, Jen," said Carol, "I only said *if* I didn't want to vote
for you. I might want to, you know."

"Mrs. McKay," said Nancy, "I still think it means you can't be
trusted to be honest about the way you vote if you have to do it
secretly."

"Not really, Nancy. A Guide *tries* to keep all the Guide laws. It
doesn't mean she always succeeds. The older you get, the more
you learn about what they mean and how hard it is sometimes to
keep them. We don't try to make it hard for someone to vote
honestly. We try to make it as fair as possible.

"It's the way people vote for mayor and Members of Parliament, too, you know. If the government didn't have that rule,
people could force others to vote for them by bribing them with
money. That wouldn't happen in Guides, but there are lots of
ways people try to make others do something they don't want to
do."

Nancy looked thoughtful. "I guess that's right. Anyhow, if a
Guide is supposed to be a friend to all and a sister to every Guide,
then you'd be bound to hurt somebody's feelings because you
can't vote for everybody."

Mrs. McKay talked to them about the Guide Promise. When
they were discussing how they could do their duty to God, they
decided that thinking about how they could love and serve God
and their neighbour made it easier to understand. Treating others
the way they themselves wanted to be treated, sounded like a
good place to start.

They discovered that among the seven of them, they belonged to four different churches and one synagogue. Then one girl said she didn't really belong to a church, but her mother always said they were going to go sometime. Mrs. McKay asked if anyone had ever been to a service in a church that wasn't her own. Nobody had. So they decided to ask their parents if they could visit each other's places of worship.

The next day after school, Jenny went over to Carol's house. She liked going there because Carol had her own room. Jenny had to share hers with her little sister. She was a nuisance sometimes, and liked to hang around when Carol came over. Carol had two brothers but they were in high school, and paid little attention to her and Jenny. Carol's mother was a nurse and when she was working, Carol had to set the table and put dinner in the oven. Jenny liked helping her, even though she hated setting the table at home. It was a baby sort of job that her little sister could do. She'd rather learn to cook.

"Weren't those skits on the Guide Law neat last night, Carol? I really liked the one your group did about smiling and singing. Especially when you broke the vase (it was good it was just a plastic cup) and said you couldn't sing, and started to whistle. And when the girl who played your mother came in and said, 'Rah-ly Miranda, it isn't ladylike to whistle. Is that my best vahse? Now don't let me hear you whistling again.' I just about cracked up. I sure wish I could whistle. I must have the wrong kind of teeth."

"It's easy. I didn't want to do that part at first because I really can sing and I like singing, but I was the only one who could whistle. We were going to have a skit about a girl whose horse dies, but nobody could smile and sing if that happened. We all thought you *had* to cry when really bad things happen to you, so we decided to do it about something that didn't matter so much.

"I bet you could learn to whistle. Let me see your teeth. Yeah, maybe you're right. My teeth have this big gap between the front ones. I can get a dime between them. Even a thin quarter. My dad says I'm going to get one stuck there sometime. I didn't tell him I almost did once. My mum says the dentist would kill me if he saw me doing it."

Carol sprawled across the bed with her head hanging over the side. "D'you ever do this?" she asked. "It makes your head feel all funny. Mum says it's because the blood rushes to your brain and that's what you should do if ever you feel like fainting."

"Suppose there isn't a bed near?" asked Jenny doubtfully.

"I don't mean you have to lie on a bed. Just put your head down lower than the rest of you. Hold it between your knees and then you usually stop feeling faint because the oxygen in your blood comes to your brain. It's a lack of oxygen that makes you feel faint. That's what my mum told me. it would be neat to be a nurse. But I think I'd rather be a doctor; they get to do more interesting things."

"I don't know what I'll be. My mother says it's too early to make up my mind. She likes me to try doing all sorts of different things."

"I don't really know either," said Carol. "Did I tell you my grandmother is going to buy me my Guide uniform? She used to be a Guide in the olden days. When she phoned on Sunday, I told her about me going to Guides. She said when she was a Guide she had to wear long black stockings all the time and heavy navy blue pants they called bloomers under her Guide dress. She even went camping in the summertime, and they didn't have any running water or electricity or anything. Not even sleeping bags. They used blankets and once they put straw in some kind of cloth bag for sort of a mattress. She's going to send me some old pictures she has of her at camp."

"You're lucky. My mum says I have to pay for half my uniform out of my allowance. But she's going to get it this week and let me pay her back."

"When do you think we'll get enrolled?"

"Next month sometime, I guess. We have some more things to learn. Remember Mrs. Mac asked us to think of ways we can do

our duty to the Queen and our country for next week? She told us we might find some ideas if we looked in the newspaper."

"Oh yeah," said Carol thoughtfully. "Let's look now. Wait'll I put the oven on for the casserole."

Carol got the casserole out of the refrigerator, turned on the oven and then started looking for the newspaper.

"I can't find it anywhere. I bet Dave took it."

"Let's go ask him. Maybe he'll help us."

"My brother? He'll tell us not to bother him. All he ever does is shut himself in his room and play records. Boy, when I'm seventeen, I'm not going to sit around all day doing that."

They went to see Dave anyway. He was at his desk, doing homework, with the record player beside him at top volume. Raising their voices, the girls told him what they wanted.

"O.K., I'm not deaf," but he turned down the volume, "and here's the newspaper. I had to find some things for my law course. Wait a minute — Canada and the Queen. Some of this might help you."

He was much more co-operative than Carol thought he would be. In fact, he seemed to like having his opinion asked. When he started telling them about what he'd been learning about the law in Canada, and how many laws there were, all to protect ordinary people, the girls were fascinated.

"How does anybody ever know all those laws so that they don't break them?" asked Jenny. "There must be dozens!"

"A lot more than dozens," answered Dave. "I don't begin to know them all. Each town, each province has its own as well as Canada as a whole. They're divided up. Some things are looked after by towns and cities, some by provinces and some big things by the Federal Government in Ottawa. Lots of laws you just know — your conscience, I guess — like not murdering somebody, but there are lots more that you'd have to look up somewhere or know about by reading the paper or learning some other way."

"I think I know what you mean," said Carol. "If we obey our country's laws, and try to find out about them, it's like doing our duty to our country, isn't it?"

"And other things too, Carol," said Jenny eagerly. "I can think of other things. What about looking after what Canada looks like? You know, not littering, and planting trees like we did at school when they built the new addition, and picking up your garbage when you go on camping trips. Some people are really awful, and destroy things."

"Just look at this in today's paper," said Dave. "It's an article about some people who were arrested for deliberately breaking up a whole bunch of picnic tables in a provincial park. Then they wrecked some people's tents who'd gone off fishing. Luckily, the park ranger caught them at it. They said they just did it for kicks because they had nothing to do."

Dave took a pile of clippings out of his notebook. "If you want to have these, you can take them. They might help you."

Carol and Jenny looked through them. "It doesn't say anything about the Queen anywhere," said Carol.

"Not exactly," agreed Dave. "But if you read some of the articles, you'll see them mention 'the Crown'. That means the

Queen and Canada all sort of tied up together. The Queen — well, I guess she stands for our country and other countries in the Commonwealth like Australia and India and Jamaica and lots more that were once British colonies, and some that still are. Originally our laws came from British law. The Queen doesn't have any real power any more; the government we elect has that. But she still protects the law and all the good things Canada stands for. The Governor General, who's a Canadian, acts on her behalf in Canada. It's confusing, but if you're doing your duty to your country, it's about the same as doing your duty to the Queen."

"Oh," said Carol, still a bit unclear. "Well, thanks Dave."

"I'm glad we thought of asking you," added Jenny. She had always wanted a big brother. It didn't seem fair that Carol had two, and didn't even appreciate them.

"Any time, kids, any time," said Dave airily, as he turned up the record player. "Who knows, they might ask me to be a Girl Guide sometime!"

Back in the kitchen, Jenny offered to set the table for Carol. She was trying to do a different sort of good turn for a different person every day. It wasn't always easy. At noon, she'd gone on an errand for Mrs. Foster next door. Since her bike had a flat tire, she'd had to walk and carry the heavy bag of groceries. Mrs. Foster had insisted on paying her. Jenny was torn between the desire to keep the money to go towards her uniform, and the awareness that a 'paid job' wasn't exactly a good turn. That's what Mrs. Mac had told them. "Something done cheerfully, willingly and without pay for somebody else" was how she'd put it. So Jenny had taken the money and decided to look for someone else for whom to do a good turn.

The only thing Jenny didn't like about going to Carol's house was the fact that she had to walk home alone. It wasn't that far, but Jenny found herself wishing that Carol lived next door.

"We could send each other secret messages," she thought. "We could put a string from our bedroom windows and send messages along it in a tin attached to it. We could even write them in lemon juice and nobody would know."

Jenny had read in a book once that if you wrote in lemon juice instead of ink, it was invisible until you held it over a light bulb or something hot. She must remember to try it sometime to see if it really worked.

Without really noticing what she was doing, she found herself kicking fallen leaves along the sidewalk. There was something hard among the leaves. Bending over, she brushed the leaves aside and found a small leather case. She opened it. Inside was a gold watch. It looked very old, and at the sides of the watch face diamonds sparkled. Someone must have lost it, and maybe she would get a reward for finding it!

Jenny ran the rest of the way home. "Mum!" she called as soon as she opened the door. "You'll never guess what I just found. A diamond watch! I bet it's worth hundreds of dollars. How do you find out whose it is and get a reward?"

"Hold on, Jen. How do you even know there'll be a reward? Let me have a look at it."

Mrs. Evans showed it to Jenny's father. They both thought it looked like a fairly valuable watch, and it was obviously very old. Dad turned it over and found the initials 'L.D.' faintly engraved. He telephoned the police station. Jenny listened intently but couldn't tell from his side of the conversation whether or not she'd get a reward. Finally he hung up the receiver.

"They know whose watch it is," he told her. "It belongs to an elderly woman who was taking it to the jeweller's for repairs. She had it in a shopping bag and didn't know until she got there that there was a hole in the bag. She's very upset about it because her husband, who has been dead for years, had given it to her."

"Did he say anything about a reward?" asked Jenny anxiously. "She must be rich to have all those diamonds!"

"Sorry, he didn't. They're not very big diamonds, Jenny. The police officer is going to come around and get the watch and take it to the woman. She'll be happy you found it."

The police officer was a pleasant young man who asked Jenny if she'd like to go with him in the police cruiser to return the watch. There was no doubt about its owner. Mrs. Dawson had described it very thoroughly.

Mrs. Dawson lived in two rooms over a store a few blocks from Jenny's house. Jenny's heart sank when she saw the rooms. She had been looking forward to a palatial home with servants. The policeman placed the watch case in the old woman's trembling hands and Jenny told her how she had found it.

There were tears in Mrs. Dawson's eyes when she opened the case. She took out the watch and turned it over in her hands.

"You don't know how much this means to me," she said. "I lost almost everything George and I had when our farmhouse burned down twenty years ago. He had a heart attack soon afterwards and died. He gave me this watch when we were married and I was wearing it at the time of the fire. The watch stopped going this week and I didn't know whether I could afford to have it repaired."

"But it's going now," said Jenny excitedly. "Or it was. The first thing I did when I opened the case was to put it to my ear. My dad said it probably hadn't been lost long because it was still going."

Mrs. Dawson held it to her ear. "My dear, you're right."

"Maybe when I kicked it in the leaves, it started going again."

"Could be," smiled the policeman. "You never can tell with watches. Well Jenny, we'd better go now; I have to get back to the station.

Mrs. Dawson went to a chest of drawers. "I haven't got very much, but I would like you to have this." She held out a silver chain with something hanging from it. "This is a cameo. It's like a carving of someone's head. It's not worth a lot of money, but I was wearing it the night of the fire, too. It was my mother's. I'd like you to have it."

"It's just beautiful! I've never seen anything like it before. Thank you. Can I come and visit you sometime and bring my friend? Her name's Carol and we're going to try making cookies on Saturday and we can bring you some if you like."

"Of course," smiled Mrs. Dawson. "I don't have any young friends like you and I'd enjoy a visit very much."

When Jenny got home and showed her mother the cameo necklace, her mother wondered if Jenny ought to keep it. Perhaps there was someone in Mrs. Dawson's family who should have it, but Jenny's father said it doubtless meant a lot to Mrs. Dawson to be able to give it to Jenny.

"It's a lovely reward," he said.

"It sure is, Dad. I was really hoping for a lot of money, but when I saw Mrs. Dawson and how happy she was to get her watch back, I felt awful for wanting money for just returning what wasn't mine anyhow. She lives all alone, up a rickety old staircase. She hasn't got much furniture or anything. I told her Carol and I would go and visit her."

"Be careful when you go kicking leaves next time," warned her father. "You're lucky you didn't break the watch."

"Break it!" said Jenny indignantly. "When I kicked it, I made it go again. Didn't I tell you?"

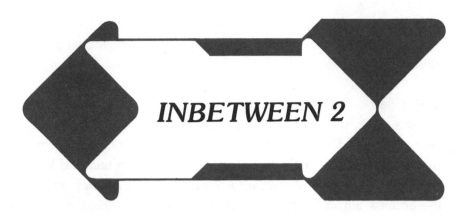

INBETWEEN 2

SHARPEN YOUR SENSES — TRY KIM'S GAME

Hearing — The game leader makes a variety of ordinary sounds while the players are either blindfolded or have their backs turned. Then they list the sounds heard. Try things like slamming a book, riffling the pages of a book, striking a match, pulling up a zipper, writing with a felt pen, snapping fingers, brushing hair, bouncing a ball, pouring water into a tin, scraping a pot. Or make up a story but just make the sounds and see if the players can tell what might have happened. Their plot might be better than yours! You might record the sounds on tape at home.

Touch — The game leader passes a variety of objects to players who are either blindfolded or have their hands open behind their backs. Or use a box (or several) with an opening in one end. The object to be felt is in the box and the players put their hands in the opening. Try a safety pin, clothes peg, comb, coins (can you tell them apart?), different fabrics, pen, paper clips, small plastic toys.

Smell — The game leader collects a variety of household liquids and solids in small bottles. A drugstore will sell you identical brown bottles at a low price. Number the bottles and keep a master list. Pass the opened bottles under the players' noses. Try vanilla, lemon rind, orange juice, peanut butter, bleach, ammonia (not too close and only for an instant), floor wax, shampoo, brown sugar, cinnamon.

Lost Coat — The game leader puts a number of items in the pockets of an old coat and pretends she has found it on a park bench. Players deduce what they can about the coat's owner from the contents of the pockets. You might include an initialled linen handkerchief, a match folder, a torn envelope that has only part of the address left, a foreign coin, a bus ticket, train schedule, and whatever you imagine will make good clues.

Dropped Purse — The game leader has a woman's purse. She drops it in clear view of all the players, letting it fall open so that all the contents spill out. Then she slowly picks up the items and puts them back in the purse. Everyone lists what she saw and deduces what she can about the owner.

Missing Action — This one, if cleverly acted out, can stump the most observant. A group acts out in mime (no words) some activity like a baseball game, a bank robbery, a lifesaving incident, or a boy asking a girl for a date. But they leave out one important part of the action. The observers have to tell what was omitted.

Seeing What You Look At All The Time — Ask the players to draw or describe accurately such common things as coins, telephone (dial or push-button), floor plan of room you meet in, floor plan of own home, what you pass on way to school or Guides, own bicycle. Does everyone know the best escape routes from different parts of her home or meeting place in case of fire?

Getting Out of The Bath — Five players who believe they can watch a series of actions and duplicate them accurately are chosen. Four leave the room. The other player watches the game leader closely. The game leader carefully goes through the necessary actions to pretend she is a woman getting out of the bath and getting dressed, like drying herself with a towel, putting on various items of clothing (struggling into a girdle is very funny), and finally admiring herself in the mirror. Then the player who has watched all this duplicates the actions as best she can in the same order, while one of the players who was sent out of the room watches. This player then repeats it for the next and so on until it has been done five or six times. Did the last actor do all the actions the first one did? If not, why?

Nature Clock — The game leader has twelve natural items found outside the meeting place and which may be taken. She lays them in a circle as if they were the numbers on a clock dial. Each patrol goes out to find the same items and returns to place them in the same order.

Do you know that it helps a blind person at a meal to tell her where things are on her plate in relation to a clock face? For example, the potatoes might be at twelve o'clock, the meat at four o'clock, the carrots at eight o'clock and so on.

To describe the position of a bird in a tree so that someone else can spot the bird quickly, think of the front of the tree as as clock face. If you can say something like 'I see a yellow warbler at two o'clock in the tree', the person knows almost exactly where it is.

FINDING A BIRD IN A TREE

Artists Observe — very closely. If you are painting something from nature, you learn to be very observant.

Try this: Go outdoors and look at something you think of as ordinary: a tree, a rock, a cloud, a house, almost anything. After a brief look, write down a description of it in terms of colour and shape. Then go out to draw or paint the same object. If your aren't using colour, write in the colours you see. Compare your final drawing with your first description. Did you see many more colours than you had thought were there?

SIMPLE FIRST AID

Every Guide should know how to treat simple injuries. She should know how to find out what the injury is and be able to decide quickly if she knows how to treat it, or if she must send for medical help. Below is a chart of injuries you should be able to look after, at least until further help is available.

INJURY	TREATMENT
bleeding from a wound	Immediately apply firm, direct pressure, by using your fingers or hand to press hard, directly on the wound (unless there is glass in it). Do not remove pressure for five minutes, or until bleeding has stopped. Apply a commercial gauze and adhesive bandage to a small wound, or gauze pad and adhesive if larger. If bleeding does not stop, get medical help.

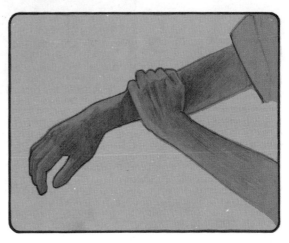

INJURY	TREATMENT
scratch or surface wound	Wash with clean water, apply first aid ointment and cover with a gauze and adhesive bandage.
poison ivy	Learn to recognize the plant and avoid it! If you come in contact with it, wash as soon as possible using laundry soap. Be thorough. This usually prevents poison ivy blisters from appearing. If the blisters appear (at least a day after exposure), apply calomine lotion. If severe, contact doctor.

insect sting	Remove stinger, if visible, with tweezers. Apply antiseptic or baking soda paste. Mix baking soda with a little water.

INJURY	TREATMENT
simple burn and sunburn	Immediately place burned portion in cold water or cold milk and keep there until pain eases. If red or blistered, cover lightly with bandage. Do not break blisters or apply lotions.

INJURY	TREATMENT
frostbite	If the skin is *chalky white*, usually in small patches on ears, cheeks, or fingertips, you know the patient is suffering from frostbite. Parts of the body become numb when frostbitten and often the person is unaware of it. Do not rub. Do not apply snow. Warm affected part as gradually as possible. Frozen fingertips are best put under one's armpits and warmed with body warmth.

INJURY	TREATMENT
sliver	Remove with tweezers or sterile needle.
nosebleed	Seat person upright with head slightly forward. Keep her mouth open in order for her to breathe. Pinch nose gently, but firmly, just below the hard part, or have the patient do this. Keep this pressure applied until bleeding has stopped.
fainting	Place patient so that the head is lower than the heart. Loosen clothing at neck and waist. Make sure the patient has fresh air.

bruise	Apply a cold compress (cloth wrung out in cold or ice water) to relieve pain.

SECRET MESSAGES

Writing in lemon juice is one way of sending a message secretly. If you write in English, anyone who knows the lemon juice trick can read it. There are many ways of making secret codes that may puzzle the reader. This is called cryptography.

The easiest way is to write out the alphabet from 'A' to 'Z'. Underneath it, write the alphabet from 'Z' backwards to 'A', like this:

A B C D E F G H I J K L M N O P Q R S T U V W X Y Z
Z Y X W V U T S R Q P O N M L K J I H G F E D C B A
A=Z, B=Y, etc.

Can you figure out this message?

HKRVH FHFZOOB HVMW GSVRI NVHHZTVH RM XLWV

Probably the next easiest method is to make each letter equal the letter next to it, like this:

A B C D E F G H I J K L M N O P Q R S T U V W X Y Z
Z A B C D E F G H I J K L M N O P Q R S T U V W X Y

Make up a message using this code.

Another method is to think of a word in which no letters are duplicated, like PLANET. These letters go at the beginning of your secret 'alphabet', and are followed by the ordinary sequence of letters, omitting those which appear in 'planet'.

P L A N E T B C D F G H I J K M O Q R S U V W X Y Z
A B C D E F G H I J K L M N O P Q R S T U V W X Y Z
P=A, L=B, etc.

You will notice that some of the letters are the same as the ordinary alphabet. 'Planet' is not the best word for this (but makes it easier to decode). Choose a longer word, whose letters come from all parts of the alphabet. Experiment and you'll see how it works.

Some messages are put into picture form. People who do not have a written language, but only a spoken one, can put long messages into pictures. Sometimes, we use a combination of pictures and letters. What does this message say?

If you are trying to figure out a cryptic message (known as 'cracking the code'), it's handy to know the most commonly used letters in the English language. One extensive survey found these were the ten most common letters:

Most common (in order):   E T R I N O A S D L
Least common: Z J Q K X

You know that a single letter is almost bound to be 'a', 'i' or 'o'. Other very common words and therefore good clues, are 'the', 'and', 'is', 'are', 'to'.

Non-Secret Codes

There are also codes which are not meant to be secretive. They are meant to pass on a message when ordinary means of communication by voice or writing are impossible.

If you were a Brownie, you may have learned semaphore. Or you may have learned finger spelling, one method of communication used by deaf people.

People who are blind learn Braille, a system of arranging raised dots on heavy paper. Each letter of the alphabet has its own arrangement of dots, and these are read by running the fingertips over them from left to right, just as you are reading this. Braille can be read as quickly as you can read this. Braille books are large and bulky because of the heavy paper necessary. This is how 'Girl Guides of Canada' looks in Braille.

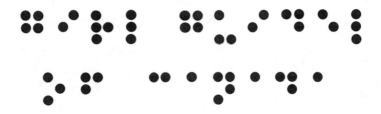

A very efficient means of communication is the Morse code where letters are indicated by dots and dashes. These can be signalled by hand-tapping, on a machine, with lights, or even visually. During World War II, the opening notes of Beethoven's Fifth Symphony were often used as a symbol for victory, because the first four notes (three short notes followed by a long note) sounded like 'v' in Morse code.

SOS, spelled out in Morse code ... — — — ..., is a widely-known message meaning 'Help!' Can you signal it with a flash-light, or tap it out on an empty can?

Ground-Air Emergency Code

There are symbols which can be used by people lost in an air crash or similar emergency, in isolated terrain. The symbols should be made very large against a contrasting background so that searchers in low-flying aircraft can spot them. They can be stamped out (fairly deeply to provide contrasting shadows) in snow-covered terrain. They can be made with branches or logs. They can be drawn (again, widely and deeply) in sand.

Require Doctor Serious Injuries	I	Am proceeding in this direction	↑	Require map and compass	□
Require food and water	F	Require medical supplies	II	Not understood	⅃L
Probably safe to land here	△	Unable to proceed	X	No	N
Require firearms and ammunition	∨∨	All well	LL	Yes	Y

1907
BROWNSEA
ISLAND.
ENGLAND

"Shut the door — everybody'll see us!" A dozen voices spoke at once as Jenny held open the door between the kitchen and the meeting hall for Carol to bring in a large mirror.

"I'm trying to be quick," said Carol. "I don't want to drop this." She propped the mirror against the wall at the back of the counter. "There are a lot of people out there already. It looks like practically everyone's mother and father must have come."

The kitchen was filled with Guides, some getting into a strange variety of costumes, some applying make-up, some putting last-minute touches on signs and props. Mrs. McKay was in a corner, looking more than slightly frazzled as she and Cathy looked at the script.

The idea for this evening had snowballed. Cathy and some others had been working on a skit about the early days of Guiding. The cast, which had begun with five girls working on the Guide History Badge, grew swiftly as the plot became more complicated. Within three weeks, the whole company was involved as actors or stagehands. From a skit it changed to a dramatic presentation! They had long discussions about a title for it and finally had written invitations to parents and friends to attend *It's the Girls' Game Too!*

The recruits had a starring role. The finale was to be their enrolment. Mrs. Mac had been concerned about their being too nervous in front of a large audience, but they had assured her that they wouldn't be.

"What if somebody is nervous?" said Cathy. "It will show the audience that Guides aren't perfect. We wouldn't want them to get the wrong impression, you know!"

The Guides who had make-up on, crowded around the mirror. Sandy Green twitched her mouth.

"This moustache is driving me crazy!" she exclaimed. "Why couldn't Baden-Powell have shaved it off?" She straightened her shoulders in an attempt at military dignity. "I must say I look pretty good. But between these woollen shorts and this moustache, I'm getting awfully itchy. Isn't it almost time to start?"

Cathy looked at her watch. "Five minutes to curtain time, or whatever you call it when you don't have a curtain. I just peeked out, and there isn't a bit of space left around the wall. There are even little kids sitting on the floor. I hope they don't come onto the stage area, or you 'Scouts' will have to do the old keep-back-the-crowds trick with your staves."

Some girls, hair pushed back under old-fashioned Boy Scout hats, grinned. "Since the six of us are supposed to be eleven thousand boys, I expect we could keep back some little kids."

One of the girls held out her wooden staff, borrowed from the Boy Scout troop. "I wish we had these. Think of all the things you could do with them! Poke your little brother, measure things, use them for stretchers, jump over streams..."

"Girls — please. It's just about time to begin." Mrs. Weston had come into the kitchen. "We've found seats for everyone, so the ushers can now be the singers. Marilyn is going to stand on the end so that if she has to help a latecomer, she can. The signpost girl is ready, and we've double-checked to make sure the signs are in the right order this time. Just two things — and I know I've said them a million times — say your lines slowly and clearly, and remember to move around enough so that all the audience gets a chance to see the front of you. There are people all around the hall."

Everyone smiled. Mrs. Weston had given those two warnings at least *two* million times.

"You all look great," she said. "If you're half as good as you were at the practice last Saturday, you'll make all the parents out there wish they were Guides."

She looked at her watch, nodded at Mrs. Mac and said, "O.K. Cathy. You're on!"

The signpost girl, stationed at one end of the hall, raised the first of her reversible signs. It read 'England — 1857'. Cathy walked slowly to the lectern near the signpost. The group of singers, sitting cross-legged on the floor near the door, began to hum 'The Guide Marching Song'. For a moment Cathy thought she was going to lose her voice. All those butterflies in her stomach were having a battle. Her mother's face, with a big encouraging smile, was suddenly in front of her and Cathy smiled back. She looked at the sign, and began to read.

**ENGLAND
1857**

"*England — 1857. Robert Stephenson Smyth Baden-Powell was born, a red howling baby . . .*" The tape-recorded cry of the Ranger Guider's young baby was heard above the fading humming of the singers. "*He seemed quite ordinary at the time, but he grew up to do extraordinary things. His father died when he was little and his mother was left with five boys and a daughter, Agnes, to raise. She must have been a fantastic mother because she let them do all sorts of exciting things. At home they called Robert Baden-Powell 'Ste'.*"

The sign changed, and three Guides, dressed as boys in loose shirts and long baggy shorts, came out carrying a brown cardboard rowboat.

ABOUT
1869

"I say," said one, "it's time we let Ste do the cooking. If he's going to come sailing with us this summer around the coast, he had better do something useful."

"Yes, " replied the tallest boy gruffly, "at school he managed to snare a rabbit, cook it, and put out the fire without the teacher catching him, but that's not quite what we need aboard ship. Ste, d'you hear?"

"Aye, aye sir! I'll practise so I'll be prepared."

ABOARD SHIP A
FEW MONTHS
LATER

The young Baden-Powell, Ste, was bent over a cardboard box with a real pot on it, which had been hastily brought on by a prop girl.

"This stove isn't much good," Ste muttered. "Not like Mother's. Not half as good as a fire out in the open. But this *has* to be good stew." Ste poked his finger in the pot, put it in his mouth and made a terrible face, amid laughter from the audience. "I wonder if cooks ever feel hungry? I sure don't. Must be this rolling sea." Ste rocked back and forth as the singers sang a sea chanty.

The brothers came close, wrapped in raincoats. "It's rough in those waves on deck. I could eat a horse. Is dinner ready, Ste?"

Ste pushed the pot towards his brothers. "It's all yours."

Grabbing spoons, they dug in. After the first taste, they put down the spoons in disgust. "Whatever did you do to it? Nobody could eat that!"

"Nobody?" said one brother. "If Ste cooked it, he can eat it! And he jolly well better! Then next time he'll cook it properly."

The brothers sat and glowered. Ste pretended to down the contents of the pot, grimacing all the time.

Cathy took up the story again. *"Robert Baden-Powell grew up, learning many things through experience, and sometimes through failing before managing to succeed. He developed many skills: acting and mimicking, sketching, hiking, boating, and by careful observation of the countryside, how the birds and animals lived. He probably learned more out of school than in school. He was never noted for good marks."*

1878
WITH THE BRITISH
ARMY IN INDIA

Sandy gave her moustache one last twitch and marched as straight as she could to the middle of the hall. "Those rascals have been stealing our horses again! The colonel has asked me to see if I can find out who is responsible."

She walked slowly around the hall, eyes glued to the floor, occasionally stopping with one hand behind an ear to listen. Suddenly she pulled a magnifying glass from her pocket, and bent down.

"Aha! I knew it! It's one of those tribesmen from the hills. Here's the blossom of a flower that grows only there. It must have stuck to his foot when he was untethering the horse. Tonight I can go there, under cover of darkness, and get our horses back. I'll ask for some volunteers to go with me."

**1900
MAFEKING, AFRICA
DURING THE BOER
WAR**

"B-P's regiment had been in various parts of the great continent of Africa for some years when war broke out between the British and the Boers, the descendants of Dutch settlers in South Africa. B-P was in charge of Mafeking, an important town which he was determined to defend against the Boers."

As Cathy spoke, two girls wheeled in a recognizable cardboard replica of a Boer gun. Dressed as Boer soldiers, they took their places with the gun. B-P strode around, stopping occasionally to peer through field glasses. A small group, dressed as men, women and children came quietly on at the end of the hall opposite the Boers. A girl pushed a bicycle past Baden-Powell.

"Young lady," said B-P briskly, "you had better go home. The Boers are beginning to shoot at us."

"Are those real shells?" she asked. "I want to stay and watch them."

"It's too dangerous," he replied. "If the Boers continue to advance you'll learn all too soon about real shells. You must go home." As the girl turned reluctantly and left, B-P continued, "She's like all the women of Mafeking, already fearless and willing, although so young."

One of the townsmen, carrying a large lantern, approached B-P.

"Ah," said B-P. "That's just what I wanted. I'm afraid of the Boers coming in by night to attack. If we had a lot of such lights, they wouldn't dare. But even with one light, perhaps we can fool them into thinking we have more lights and more men than we do. If we put this on a long pole, and carry it to different parts of the town all night long, they won't dare come in, lest our light catch them in its beam."

"Here's a pole for it, sir," said the man. "Is there some way we could make them believe we have a lot more men in Mafeking? That might frighten them."

From his knapsack, B-P took a metal tube which was wider at one end than at the other.

"This is a megaphone. When I put the small end to my mouth and speak into it, it sounds much louder. I think it's just what we need."

The lights were all turned out and the signpost girl raised a cardboard sliver of a moon with a flashlight taped to it. The girl with the lantern went from corner to corner, turning the lantern off and on. B-P raised the megaphone and called through it.

"Ready, men?" Turning the other way and changing his voice, he gave the reply, "All ready and waiting, sir." Then, "Advance silently, men."

When the lights went on again, several girls dressed as young boys ran up to Baden-Powell and spoke in turn.

"Sir, we've done all you asked us to do and more."

"We delivered all the messages faster than you thought we could."

"We took food to the soldiers so that they could stay at their posts."

"We helped carry two injured men to the hospital, and they're going to be all right."

"And we've worked out a better plan to get the ammunition out safely at night to our men at the guns."

"Well done, lads. There's no doubt that you boys have done a tremendous job in helping to defend Mafeking. We've managed to hold off the enemy for almost seven months. Surely our British troops will arrive soon to rescue us."

The lights went off again and the singers began to hum a martial air, breaking off to shout "Hip, hip, hooray!" before Cathy resumed the narration.

"*After the siege of Mafeking, Baden-Powell became a national hero in Great Britain. When he returned to England he made good use of all the things he had learned during his long military career. He soon realized that there were many boys who didn't have enough to do. Remembering all the good times he had as a boy discovering how to live in the outdoors, and the usefulness of the boys of Mafeking, he did something very daring.*"

**1907
BROWNSEA ISLAND,
ENGLAND**

A tent, (borrowed from a Guide's family and not much like the large, bulky army bell tent used by Baden-Powell) was, quickly and rather shakily, erected by a couple of Guides dressed as boys. As Cathy read, they pretended to cook. One had the bedraggled remains of a child's stuffed animal which she pretended to skin like a rabbit.

88

"Brownsea Island in Poole Harbour, Dorset, became the site of the first Scout camp in 1907, although Scouts didn't even exist then. It was here that B-P took twenty-four boys, rich and poor, put them into groups he called 'Patrols', and let them cook their own meals — even catch the food with snares and fishing lines. He taught them how to track and stalk, spun them yarns about his adventures in India and Africa, told them the kind of personal laws he lived by, and gave them fun and responsibility such as they'd never had before. The boys loved it."

1908

As the campers quietly withdrew, B-P sat down at a table quickly put into place by the prop girl. He began to write. Around the edge of the room, small groups of boys and girls bent over books and then started doing things. A couple put bandages on each other. One crouched as if stalking a wild animal. One started laying sticks for a fire.

"B-P put many of his ideas into a book which he called 'Scouting for Boys'. All over Britain the book was bought and read and the activities tried out by eager boys. This he expected, knowing boys. However, girls were just as enthusiastic about his book!"

One of the girls, who had been practising stalking, began to write a letter, reading aloud as she wrote.

"We are girls, and we can ride and swim and climb a tree and track a person. When you write back, please don't say anything about sewing and lessons and housework, because these are the things Mother says we should do and we hate them."

Baden-Powell scowled as he heard these words, and spoke testily. "Hate them indeed! Their mother's right — that's the kind of things girls were made for. Scouting's for boys, not girls. They should be learning how to be proper ladies."

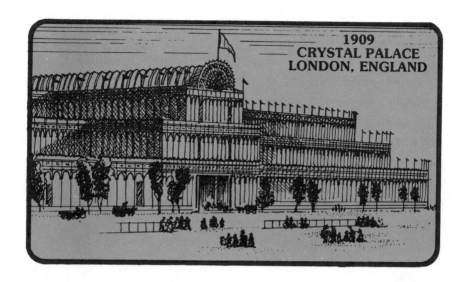

1909
CRYSTAL PALACE
LONDON, ENGLAND

"B-P had no idea how many boys were calling themselves Scouts and following the ideas in his book, so he announced a Rally at the Crystal Palace, an exhibition building in London. He said anyone doing Scouting could come."

Baden-Powell stood rigidly at attention at one side of the room. Guides dressed as boys, marched slowly across the room in front of him. At the end of the line marched several girls, dressed as girls. They wore felt hats, leather boots and skirts reaching halfway down their legs. The singers, softly at first, but increasing in volume as the girls approached B-P, sang '*We are Marching Along the King's Highway*'.

"Baden-Powell was tremendously thrilled to have eleven thousand boys parade in front of him. He felt rather differently about the little group of girls at the end."

B-P stood in front of the girls and asked, "Who are you?"

Together, standing very straight, they replied, "We are the Girl Scouts."

He turned to his sister beside him, "Agnes, what do you think of this?"

"I think you're going to have to do something about it," she replied. "They're a pretty determined lot of girls. Couldn't you write a book just for them?"

"Hmmm. How about you doing it, Agnes? You know more about girls than I do, and you seem to agree with them."

"And so Agnes, B-P's sister, wrote a handbook, 'How Girls Can Help to Build Up the Empire'. Baden-Powell suggested they be called 'Girl Guides' after the regiment of guides who had helped the army in India and were ready to take on all sorts of challenging jobs. This was how Girl Guides began. The girls themselves were determined not to be left out of the fun and adventure that their brothers were enjoying in the game of Scouting. Visitors to the British Isles learned about Guides and took this wonderful new idea home to their own countries.

**NOVEMBER 1909
ST. CATHARINES,
ONTARIO, CANADA**

Two girls walking side by side, in winter coats, talked excitedly.

"Isn't it going to be fun? We're going to be the first Canadian Girl Guides! Mrs. Malcolmson says it's the most exciting thing there's ever been for girls anywhere!"

"Wouldn't you have liked to have been at the Crystal Palace Rally she told us about and gatecrashed the boys' big parade?"

"Oh yes, but they're going to show us how to do all sorts of interesting things, like bandaging the wounded and signalling at sea, and even marching like soldiers do. I can hardly wait!"

"We'll have to decide what kind of uniforms to have. I'd like a hat you can put pleated ribbons on. What kind of shirtwaist do you think would be best? Oh — and isn't it kind of the hotel owner to let us have our meetings in the ballroom?"

"When I get home I'm going to write to my cousin. Wait until I tell her about Girl Guides! She'll be green with envy!"

**1910
GIRL GUIDES
"OFFICIAL"**

"And this was how Guiding spread all over the world. Women and girls heard about it from friends, or saw Guides when they travelled. By 1919, Girl Guides (or Girl Scouts because some countries kept the original name) had sprung up in many countries all over the world. In 1912 Robert Baden-Powell had married Olave Soames, a lovely woman much younger than himself, who soon became deeply interested in Guiding. She formed the International Council in 1919, and after its fourth meeting, the World Association of Girl Guides and Girl Scouts was born in 1928. Canada was one of the twenty-eight original members of the World Association, which first met in Hungary."

As Cathy had been reading, three girls had come on stage with the World Flag. They raised it slowly on a pole, and five more girls entered, each wearing a sandwich board. The girl whose board depicted the World Pin stood in the centre, flanked by girls with pictures of Our Chalet, Olave House, Our Cabaña and Sangam.

1930

The girl who had raised the World Flag spoke. "At the World Conference in 1930, the World Flag, designed by Froken Kari Aas of Norway, was adopted. It may be carried as company colours by Guide companies and is flown at all International events and on many national occasions, and at the World Centres."

FOUR
WORLD
CENTRES

Our Cabaña

Our Chalet

Olave House

Sangam

"The World Pin was adopted in 1946 and is the same design as the World Flag. Any member of any Girl Guide Association in the world can wear this, both in and out of uniform. The Golden Trefoil stands for the sun which shines over all Guides everywhere. The three leaves, like the three fingers used in the Guide sign when we make our Promise, stands for the three parts of the Promise. The stars in the Trefoil signify the Promise and Law which we all try to keep. The vein on the Trefoil is shaped like a compass needle, and points to the right course in life to follow. The base of the stalk of the Trefoil is the heraldic 'feu', or flame, for the love that Guides have in their hearts for people everywhere."

"I am Our Chalet, the Guide World Centre near Adelboden in the mountains of Switzerland. Through their membership all Guides own me, and may visit me to ski, mountain climb, or just enjoy the friendship of people from other countries. One of my rooms was furnished by Canada."

"I am Olave House, named after Olave, Lady Baden-Powell. I used to be called Our Ark because I was like a home away from home in London, England, for members visiting there."

1957

"I am Our Cabaña and I am the only World Centre in the Western Hemisphere. I'm near Cuernavaca, Mexico and Canadians often visit me. My visitors usually learn Mexican handicrafts and often take part in a service project for some of the villages."

1966

"I am Sangam. My name is a Sanskrit word that means 'where two rivers meet and become one'. I am near Poona, India and I represent the meeting of eastern and western cultures. When members of Guiding stay within my gracious rooms they learn much about each other's traditions and cultures."

As the four girls with the World Centre sandwich boards moved slowly to one end of the room, the singers sang the songs of the World Centres. Two prop girls placed ten blue candles on the floor near the World Pin sandwich board, whose bearer had remained near the World Flag. One large gold candle was placed in the centre. Mrs. McKay and Mrs. Weston walked quietly and stood beside it while the 'Sangam Song' finished.

All the Guides, most still wearing costume, and some in Guide uniform, formed a horseshoe facing the candles and the World Flag. The recruits were among them, each with the patrol she had decided to join. The singers who were last to take their places in the horseshoe were singing 'The World Song'.

Mrs. McKay said, "You have just seen and heard how Guiding began and grew to over seven million members in over ninety countries in almost every corner of the world.

"Tonight, seven more girls are going to make their Promise and become part of the worldwide sisterhood of Guides.

"Jane, you were the last girl to be enrolled in this company. Will you please light the Promise candle?"

Jane stepped forward and carefully lit the large gold candle. "I light this candle to remind us of the Promise. When we try to keep our Guide Promise we are helping make this world a better place for ourselves and for everyone else."

Mrs. McKay continued, "We, who promise to do our best to do our duty to God, know that God will help us as we try to carry out the Guide laws. They are not easy to keep. Listen to them."

In turn, five girls stepped forward — each lit two candles as she repeated two laws until all ten had been said. The eleven candles cast a warm glow throughout the hall.

"Heather, will you bring forward your recruit to be enrolled?"

Heather took Jenny by the hand and they stood together in front of Mrs. McKay. "I present Jenny Evans who has passed her Tenderfoot Test and wishes to be enrolled as a Guide." Heather stepped back a pace.

"Thank you, Heather." Mrs. Mac smiled at Jenny and Jenny smiled back. "I'm not the least bit scared," she thought. She heard her little sister, somewhere in the audience, say, "that's my sister", and she was glad.

"Jenny, do you know the Guide Law, and have you considered what it means?"

Jenny tried to remember what she was supposed to answer. In her mind she said, "You can trust me, Mrs. Mac, you can all trust me. The Guide Law — I think I know what it's about."

"I know the Guide Law and I believe that I understand its meaning."

"Are you ready to make the Guide Promise?"

"Yes."

"Will you promise on your honour to do your best to do your duty to God, the Queen and your country; to help other people at all times; and to obey the Guide Law?"

Jenny remembered to raise her right hand to her shoulder, fingers bent in the position of the Guide sign — three fingers for the three parts of the Promise she was about to make — and spoke loudly and clearly.

"I promise, on my honour, to do my duty to God, the Queen and my country; to help other people at all times, and to obey the Guide Law."

Mrs. Mac pinned her Tenderfoot Pin on her uniform. "I trust you, on your honour, to keep this Promise and to try to do Good Turns wherever you are." She grasped Jenny's left hand with her left hand. "You are now one of the sisterhood of Guides."

Heather gave her a Daffodil Patrol Emblem and Mrs. Weston gave her a title tape with the company name and number on it.

Jenny watched the other recruits being enrolled. They had talked about whether or not seven girls were too many to be enrolled on one occasion. "It's a long time for everyone to stand still," Mrs. Weston had said. But every one of the recruits had wanted to be part of the show's finale, and had learned what they had to know to complete the Tenderfoot Test.

After the last girl was enrolled, they all sang 'The World Song.' All but the singers were to leave quietly for the kitchen during the last few lines. The singers were going to fill in with some songs until the rest returned with juice and cookies for their guests.

As the Guides started to move off, and the song ended, a voice said, "Guides!" Startled, Jenny looked behind her. A number of girls in the audience, in white blouses, navy skirts and red and white maple leaf scarves, were standing pointing accusingly at the Guides. The voice rang through the hall.

"Guides, you have forgotten something! You left the story in-complete! What about the Brownies?"

Cathy spoke up. "The Brownies? They were the early Guides' little sisters who wanted to be Guides. So B-P started Brownies for them. We all know that story."

"And what are you going to do when you're too old for Guides?"

"Me? Well, I . . . uh . . ." said Cathy.

"You can't hang around forever, you know."

"I'll look around for something." she suggested.

"Look around? LOOK WIDE! Look wide with us!"

By now three other Guides had joined Cathy. "Who are you?" they asked.

"We're Rangers. And they've been around since about 1917. Lord Baden-Powell said Rangers were girls who looked wide because the whole world lay before them to explore. Come with us!"

The four girls looked at Mrs. McKay. The other Guides were beginning to relax. At first they thought the Rangers were going to kidnap Cathy and the other three. But now it was apparent that this had been planned with the Rangers as a way for the Guides to join their group.

"Go," said Mrs. Mac. "Cathy, Heather, Susan, Moira, go. Join Rangers and look wide. Take our best wishes and your Promise with you."

The singers started to sing 'Go Well and Safely', the Zulu Farewell that they often sang at the end of a meeting. Jenny had almost forgotten that some of the older Guides were planning to leave the Guide company to go to Rangers. She had known Heather for only a short time, but even so she felt a sadness at her leaving.

Afterwards, when Jenny and Carol were helping tidy up in the kitchen, they asked Mrs. Weston about Rangers.

"What's Rangers like?" she repeated. "Oh, the Rangers have a really good time. This group used to be a Sea Ranger crew years ago when there were Land, Sea and Air Rangers. Nowadays, Rangers are . . . well, Rangers . . . and they can do almost anything at all.

"This Ranger group owns a couple of old canoes, that they've repaired themselves; everything from making new gunwales to caning the seats. They often go on canoe trips and compete in canoe races."

"Suppose you don't like canoeing?" asked Jenny, who had never been in a boat.

"They hike a lot too — backpacking. And sometimes they work hard to raise money for a big trip. Three years ago they went to Our Cabāna in Mexico.

"To be able to afford that, they learned to quilt and made some crib quilts to sell. They held car washes, bake sales, baby-sit-ins every Saturday before Christmas so that mothers could shop without worrying about their children or paying as much as a regular sitter would cost.

"Then they do all kinds of service projects like helping with Meals-on-Wheels, getting library books for shut-ins, candy-striping at the hospital, helping at the day care centre, and they always have a project and activity with the Venturer and Rover Scouts to raise money for world hunger.

"They do other things with the boys too. Last year they had a joint winter camp combined with a winter carnival. You must have heard about that. It was even on TV. It was just after Scout-Guide Week and they challenged the mayor to go with them. They didn't think he was the outdoor type. They got a big surprise when he turned out to be able to teach them a thing or two. He used to be an instructor in survival techniques in the militia. He was really up on winter camping!"

"Wow!" said Carol. "Here I've just become a Guide and look at all the things there are to do!"

"There's lots of time in Guides to learn how to do all the things you'll want to do when you're a Ranger."

"I don't know if I want to do anything with boys though. They're creepy and spoil all your fun."

"Wait until you're fourteen. You may change your mind!" laughed Mrs. Weston. "I know I did."

PUTTING ON A SKIT

You can have lots of fun putting on a skit about things that have happened in the life of Guiding. All you need is an outline of a happening and some imagination about what it felt like being part of the happening.

For skits, no props or costumes are necessary, although it's fun to create an illusion with something as simple as a hat, a sign, a picture on a stick, or some fabric.

There are several books available from the Distribution Centre about the history of Guiding. Look in the bibliography at the end of this book. Your own Guide company or your Guide District Council may own some of these, or some books that are now out of print. Public libraries sometimes have special Guide-Scout sections which Guides or Scouts have started by donating books. If your public library doesn't have any books, show your librarian the Guide catalogue and ask if your library will buy some books you think Guides will use.

Try these happenings for skits

(i)   The courtship and marriage of Olave Soames and Robert Baden-Powell (found in *The Story of the Girl Guides* by Alix

Liddell, and in some other books): the shipboard romance of a young woman on her first trip alone and the gallant middle-aged hero.

(ii) The cruise of the liner 'Calgaric', carrying Lord and Lady Baden-Powell to many European countries in 1933 (found in *The Story of the Girl Guides*): Scouts refused to wash their hands, which B-P had shaken, until their desperate parents promised to bottle the wash water for a souvenir.

(iii) *Like Measles It's Catching* has all sorts of adventures that happened to Canadian Guides down through the years.

There are lots of other topics for skits

When you read through the badge requirements in *Guiding for You*, you will find a number of badges that include skits. Try some of these ideas.

(i) Think up emergency situations in which you could be involved and act them out. What would you do if you were snowed in, at your house in the country, your mother ill, your father stuck in the city because of blocked roads, and the power cut off? What would you do if you were baby-sitting and a stranger came to the door, claiming to be the uncle of the sleeping children you were caring for?

(ii) Your library probably has books about the early days of the community in which you live. Exciting (and funny) things often happened to our country's pioneers. Try dramatizing some of these.

(iii) Lots of things happen at camp that make good skit material. The girls who use the water from the hot water bottle to make the morning porridge might find themselves portrayed!

(iv) Try skits based on a 'punch line'. Make up a suitable last line and challenge each other to create a skit leading up to it. For example, "It was the last sound old John ever heard" or "And to think I used to be afraid of mice!"

(v) Acting out well-known TV shows in mime (no words, only movement) can be fun for others to figure out.

Steps in creating a skit

1. Read the story outline until it is clear in your mind. If you are making up your own story write down a rough outline of the sequence of events.
2. Decide what characters are needed. Don't forget that you may want people to play the part of inanimate objects like trees.
3. Decide who will play what part — preferably letting people choose their own parts — and think about what it feels like to be that person or thing.
4. 'Talk through' the story, using the kind of conversation you think might have taken place.
5. If you need a narrator to fill in bits that can't be done through conversation, write out the narration. This is called the 'continuity', because it makes the story being acted out a continuous unit, letting the audience know what's going on when the conversation alone can't make it clear.
6. Think of ways of showing where the action is taking place. Several chairs placed beside each other and covered with a blanket might be a park bench. A girl holding a tree branch, real or cardboard, creates an outdoor look. Girls holding a length of blue material (perhaps a sheet folded lengthwise) and waving it gently, make a lake or river.
7. For a skit it's best not to write out the conversation or dialogue in full because it can sound too stilted that way. If you know the

story outline well, you can say the kind of thing that might have been said quite naturally.

8. Make sure you have a solid ending to your skit. Don't let it just drift away! If you're going to bow (a good idea, if only to let the audience know it's the end!), leave your arms at your sides, bow slowly and grandly from the waist and SMILE at your audience. And welcome the applause!

What would it be like if you were somebody — or something — else?

Shut your eyes and think hard. Pretend you are somebody totally different. Or pretend you are some kind of object, or part of it. Then get into the skin of that person, or thing, and act out the feeling.

TRY BEING: an old lady in a nursing home who has her first visitor in months.

a small child whose baby-sitter spends all her time watching a television programme he doesn't like.

the most beautiful person you've ever known.

a truck driver who has just slammed on his brakes because of a careless cyclist.

a brave twelve-year-old boy who has just met a bear in the woods.

a nervous man preparing to ask a pretty girl to marry him.

a tree that someone is chopping down with an axe.

a ball being bounced by a child.

a rocket going off into space.

a diner waiting for grace to be said (with some friends).

a vacuum cleaner in a very dusty house.

WAYS OF MAKING THE STORY OF GUIDING COME ALIVE

Try writing a poem

You have probably read poems that tell a story about something that happened. This is called narrative poetry. Some kinds of story poems are called ballads. They usually have four-line verses and sometimes are sung.

Poetry can be rhyming or non-rhyming. It can have a definite rhythm (or metre), or it can be free verse with no special rhythm. The most important thing about poetry, indeed what makes it poetry, is that you take care with the words and choose the best ones to express what you mean. Find a book of poetry and look for examples of narrative poems — ones that tell a story — to help you get the feel of it. Read them out loud. Poetry is meant to be read aloud.

Then try writing a poem about Guiding!

Try making a comic strip

Turn the story you want to tell into a series of pictures in a strip. Pictures can be as simple as stick figures, or you can make them more detailed. Remember the 'balloons' that contain what people say.

Try a puppet show

Wouldn't it be fun to turn the story of Guiding into a puppet show? There are all kinds of ways to make puppets and stages.

Try making up a game about Guiding

Card games and board games you are familiar with can be adapted for this. Do you ever play 'Concentration'? You turn the cards face down, and in turn the players turn over two cards. If they are a pair, the player keeps them and tries again; otherwise the next person plays. Make Concentration cards with Guiding information on them, for example, 'Brownsea Island' and 'First Scout Camp' would be a pair, or '1857' and 'B-P's birth'.

Try making a filmstrip

Do you like to draw? Do you know someone with a camera that takes good coloured slides? If you do, tell about Guiding by making a filmstrip of your drawings. This is a good activity for a group.

1. Decide what parts of the story you can illustrate. Make a storyboard — a series of squares like this.

Title	Brownsea Island	Reading Scouting for Boys	Crystal Palace	First Girl Scout	B-P Shocked	Agnes Baden-Powell	First Guide	Credits

In them, write down, in order, what the pictures will be about.

2. Draw the pictures on large sheets of white paper or Bristol board. Make the colours good and strong, clearly outlined. Crayons or oil pastels are suitable for use.

3. Make sure your pictures are in the right order. You may want your first picture to be a title picture, and your last one a list of credits, naming the artists, photographer and script writer.

4. Ask your friend with the camera to photograph each picture in the right order using good lighting, making sure that all the pictures

you have drawn are photographed. Slide films have either twenty or thirty-six pictures, so choose either number of pictures to be photographed.

5. When you have the film developed, ask that the slides not be mounted. That way, they will be returned to you in a strip that can be projected onto a screen using a filmstrip projector. (Of course, you can have them mounted instead and show them as slides using a slide projector.)

6. Write a short script to fit the pictures and you're all set.

DO YOU KNOW...?

That Guides and Scouts use a left handshake? When Lord Baden-Powell lived in West Africa he heard a story about two neighbouring tribes. They had been enemies for a long time. There had been much loss of life. One day, they decided that to live in peace together would be far better. Thus, they threw down their shields which they carried on their left arms to protect themselves. Now defenceless, they walked towards each other, left hands outstretched in friendship, each trusting the other. Thus the left handshake has always been a sign of trust and friendship among Guides and Scouts all over the world.

That Olave, Lady Baden-Powell was made World Chief Guide in 1930? Until the 1972 World Conference, the only one held in Canada, Lady Baden-Powell had never missed such an event. Even then, at the age of eighty-three, she sent a telephone message of greeting to the delegates. For many years she lived at Hampton Court Palace. There she had a Grace-and-Favour Apartment (given rent free for her use by the Queen, who is herself a former Brownie, Guide and Ranger). One of the rooms had been slept in by Shakespeare! On the walls hung many fine sketches and paintings done by Lord Baden-Powell.

That Lady Baden-Powell never went to school? Her father thought that she could learn as much at home and in the countryside surrounding the many homes in which they lived throughout her girlhood. She had lessons in a variety of things from different people, however. She learned to play the violin well and loved music. After she was grown up, married, very busy with Guiding and needing money, she asked a friend to sell her much-loved violin, which she called 'Diana'. The friend was indeed a friend. She bought 'Diana' herself and then donated it to the British Girl Guides for the use of any Guide violinist. Since then violins and other musical instruments have been donated to the British Girl Guides for the same purpose.

That Canadian Girl Guide Headquarters is in a lovely, three-story building at 50 Merton Street in Toronto, Ontario? Members of Guiding in Canada raised the money to build it by buying 'square inches' of the building. It has offices, meeting rooms, a shop selling Guide supplies, and a Distribution Centre with shipping facilities and storage for uniforms, books, and supplies which are sent all across Canada. If you are ever in Toronto, be sure to visit your National Headquarters.

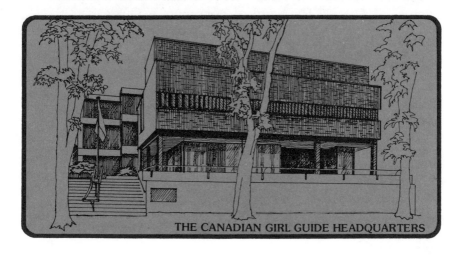

THE CANADIAN GIRL GUIDE HEADQUARTERS

DO YOU RECOGNIZE THESE GUIDE LAWS?

Each of the Guide Laws below comes from a different country.
Write down the appropriate Canadian Guide Law.

Australia	A Guide makes good use of her time.
Italy	A Girl Scout obeys her parents, teachers, leaders, and knows when it is necessary to take the initiative.
United States	I will do my best... to show respect for myself and others through my words and actions.
Mexico	A Guide looks after animals and plants and sees in nature the work of God.
Greece	She has courage and does not panic.
France	A Girl Scout likes to work and does not fear endeavour, does nothing by halves.
Cyprus	The word of honour of a Guide is to be believed and respected.
Kuwait	The Girl Guide is sincere towards her country, her parents, her seniors and her juniors.
Upper Volta	A Guide, sister to every other Guide, is available to all.
United Kingdom of Great Britain and Northern Ireland	A Guide is polite and considerate.

Have you heard of the '11th Guide Law'?

The following story is told in *The Wolf That Never Sleeps*, a story of Baden-Powell by Marguerite de Beaumont, now out of print.

"The Chief [Baden-Powell] arrived at Foxlease [a British Guide Training Centre] one day with a parcel under his arm. It turned out to be a framed copy of the Guide Law beautifully written out in script by himself. Directly he had unpacked it everyone noticed that there were eleven instead of ten Guide Laws written out. The eleventh was 'A Guide is not a fool'. He used to say the same with Scouts, too. I asked him what made him think of adding this law, and he said: 'First, because it is a good one and makes you pull yourself together and think, when you are about to do something stupid; and, secondly, because I once saw a lot of Guides in the pouring rain without coats and they told me they were hardening themselves off! To be hardy is a good thing, to be foolhardy is no good at all!' "

THE WORLD IS ALL AROUND YOU

You are a member of a patrol, which is part of a Guide company, which belongs to a District, which is part of a Division, which is . . . Look at the ever-widening circles, and you'll see they end with the World Association of Girl Guides and Girl Scouts — WAGGGS.

Fill in the name of your patrol and company. Find out the names of all the other parts of the circles and fill them in. You might like to put something else in the circle too, like a tiny provincial floral emblem, or your Commissioners' names, or something that reminds you of your District.

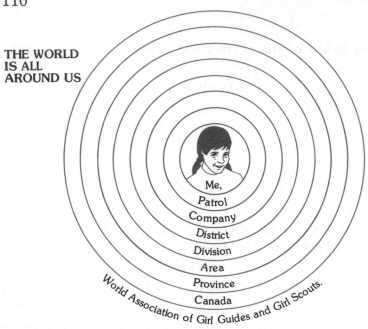

THE WORLD
IS ALL
AROUND US

Me,
Patrol
Company
District
Division
Area
Province
Canada
World Association of Girl Guides and Girl Scouts.

A Guide Meeting for the whole world!

Every three years there is a World Conference. Each member country sends two delegates who are allowed to vote. Full Members of WAGGGS vote on every issue, but Associate Members (countries not quite ready for the responsibilities of full membership, something like recruits being a recruit) do not vote on policy or financial matters.

Member countries must:

(1) Have a Promise and Law that mean the same as the original Promise and Law laid down by the Founder, Lord Baden-Powell.

(2) Allow any girl of any nationality, race, creed or circumstance to join if she chooses.

(3) Be independent of any political organization or party.

(4) Pay an annual quota and submit an annual report.

Princess
Tonie

The late April sun was high in the sky and hotter than the girls had thought possible when they set out on a hike after breakfast. It was hard to believe that only three weeks ago there had still been snow on the ground. Now the early wildflowers were in bloom and others were pushing through the ground cover of dead leaves.

"It's so hot and I'm thirsty," said Kim. "Can't we stop for a rest? This knapsack gets heavier every step."

"Yes," agreed Carol. "If I ate the food in mine, it would be easier to carry."

Lynn, the new Daffodil Patrol Leader and some of her patrol, along with a couple of other Guides, were hiking downriver from town. Most of them were working on parts of different outdoor badges, but their chief reason for choosing that particular Saturday for their hike was a news item Lynn had spotted in the newspaper.

'Farmers Near Mud Creek Irate Over Beaver Return', the head-line had read. For the first time in many years beavers were living in the vicinity and had succeeded in building a dam across a small creek that emptied into the river along which the girls were hiking. The dam was threatening to flood the farmers' fields and pastures. One farmer was reported to have put an old bedspring across a culvert, hoping it would keep out the beaver. The wily animal had found the bedspring a perfect frame for his dam-building and created a superlative structure on it.

"When do we get to Mud Creek where the beavers are?" asked one of the girls plaintively. She hadn't been able to borrow a knapsack and was tired of changing her bag of supplies from one hand to the other. She could have put her things in someone else's knapsack and shared the carrying of the double load. But she thought it would be easier to carry her half of the load in her hands. Now she was having second thoughts. The knapsacks didn't seem to be giving the girls too much trouble, despite Kim's complaint.

"It's about another mile by my calculations — and this map," said Lynn. "Look, why don't we sit down on the river bank here and have a lemonade rest? Did you all bring some raisins like I suggested? If we climb up the bank, there's a grassy spot to lie on that doesn't look too damp. Anyhow, most of us have ground sheets."

Looking much happier, and their loads feeling suddenly lighter, the girls scrambled up the bank. The lemonade was refreshing and the raisins filled the empty spaces. Jenny lay on her ground sheet with her head hanging over the bank and watched while more energetic ones in the group threw stones in the river. She poked the vertical walls of the bank idly with a stick. Lynn lay down beside her.

"Hey Jen, there's something in there. I can see something pink."

Jenny leaned over further. The edge of some pink glass showed where she had been making a hole in the bank. She enlarged the hole carefully while Lynn slid down the bank.

"It's part of a dish or something. Haven't we got something better do dig with?"

"I've got a big metal spoon in my knapsack," said Melanie, who had just joined them.

With the spoon and some sticks the three girls dug excitedly into the bank. Soon they had uncovered a number of pieces of glass, china and pottery. Most of the items were broken or at least badly cracked.

"What's this funny-looking cup?" Jenny held up a mug with a broken handle. Across the top of the mug was a shelf with a hole in it.

"I know what that is," said Melanie. "That's a moustache cup. My aunt collects them. In the olden days when men had big handlebar moustaches, they drank out of that kind of cup. That ledge thing kept their moustaches out of their tea. Isn't it funny?"

"I never heard of them. Sounds like a good idea if you have a moustache!"

"Here are some old medicine bottles. They're not even broken. Are they ever full of mud! Look! One even has a label and you can read the name of the store on it. How did all this stuff get here anyhow?"

Lynn pointed to farm buildings in the distance. "That's probably a really old farm and maybe they used to bring the garbage that wouldn't burn down to the end of their farm here. Then it gradually got covered over or else the farmer covered it over on purpose. This part along the river doesn't really belong to any of the farmers. It's public. But anyhow, this stuff is really old, that's for sure. I bet it's been here since 1900!"

By this time all the Guides were examining the find and digging around for more pieces. Lynn got a plastic bag from her pack and placed the better pieces in it. The rest were put back and covered up again.

It wasn't long before they reached the place where Mud Creek flowed into the river. Before exploring the beavers' work, the girls decided to cook lunch. Finding firewood was easy. There were lots of dead weed tops from last autumn, and fallen branches from winter storms. Many of the trees were willow and poplar, which they knew didn't burn well, but there were other trees too. An old, gnarled apple tree had lots of dead wood on and around it.

"Since there are eight of us, how about making two fires and sharing them?" suggested Lynn.

It worked out well. Five girls had foil dinners or stick dinners to cook, and used one fire. The rest needed a grate for pans. They made a hunter's fire, using the light grate that Lynn had brought.

Carol and Jenny were trying shish kebabs. On green sticks they impaled pieces of tomato, Polish sausage and onion. When the flames had died down to a steady intense heat, they turned their food-laden sticks over and over carefully, above the coals, until the food had browned and was sizzling. Then they slid the sticks' contents quickly into open hot dog buns.

"This is good," said Jenny, surprised at her own success. "I'm going to heat my next bun in a piece of foil so that it'll be hot too. If I could balance two sticks at once I could do it on a stick too, but I'm afraid to try." She looked at Melanie, who was breaking an egg into an orange peel. "What's that? Whatever are you doing?"

Melanie didn't look up. "Wait a minute. This is tricky."

She put the orange peel, with the raw egg in it, cautiously into the hots coals at the fire's edge. "I read it in a book, but I've never tried it before. You cut an orange in half, eat the pulp, then put an egg in the empty skin and cook it until it's set. I've got a neat thing for the other half of the orange too." She held up a small plastic container. "This has gingerbread mix in it. I use the orange skin for a cake pan to cook it. It'll be like a ginger cupcake with an orange flavour from the 'pan'. Or a burnt flavour, if I'm not careful! This egg is practically cooked already."

The other two Guides using the fire sat on a log, munching their hot dogs. "We'd rather be safe than sorry," they said. "All that fancy stuff! With a hot dog you can't go wrong."

At that moment the log rolled backwards and both girls fell off amid shrieks. Two hot dogs lay in the mud.

"You can't?" laughed the rest.

"We've got more. But what a waste! This was cooked just right. Maybe I can scrape off the mud. Yuck!"

When all evidence of the two fires had been cleaned up, and the little bit of garbage put into plastic bags for carrying home, the girls began to explore their surroundings.

"I've found some tracks!" called one of them excitedly. "They almost look like little kids' hands."

"Don't step on them," warned Lynn. "That sounds like raccoon tracks and I've got some plaster of Paris to make casts. There's enough for everybody to do it if you want."

There were lots of clear raccoon tracks not far from the water's edge. Lynn showed them all how to make the creamy plaster and pour it into cardboard collars around the tracks. They left them to harden while they followed the creek as far as a farmer's fence.

Carol pointed further up the creek. "That must be the beaver dam. What a pile of stuff! It looks as if he's cut down half the woods. Let's go over the fence. It's all broken down and it'll be easy to climb over."

"Let's not," said Lynn. "That's private property."

"The farmer will never know. It's a long way back to his house."

"So? That's not the point. You wouldn't like it if people came tramping all over your backyard. And it isn't any different for the farmer. With a fence like this, he doesn't need it broken down any more."

Carol looked grumpy. "I bet he wouldn't even care."

"Want to hike back around to the road and ask him?" said Melanie. "It's only about four miles there and back."

"O.K.," said Carol in a resigned tone of voice. "But I still think you're making a fuss over nothing."

Lynn was getting exasperated. "Well, we're not. You should *know* some farmers and hear all the stupid things some people do. They even go right into their cornfields and steal corn in the fall, by the truckload sometimes. They go into their woods and hunt and leave a big mess. All kinds of things. And it all starts with having attitudes like yours."

Fortunately, there was a distraction just then. One of the girls had walked across a fallen log and some rocks to the other side of the creek's mouth, and was calling.

"You should see this! Come on over! You can see where the beavers have cut down a bunch of little trees!"

Arguments forgotten, the girls balanced their way on the log across the creek. Just beyond a tangle of willows was a small grove of poplar trees. Many were cut off a short way above the ground. A few felled trunks lay scattered around.

"Is that ever sharp!" breathed Melanie admiringly. "Those beavers have cut every one at the same angle!"

"Sharp is right," laughed Lynn. "All by teeth too! Gosh, you'd think they'd been to Guide camp. Every piece is cut at a 45 degree angle. Like putting in tent pegs!"

Carol picked up a short thick piece, with beaver teeth marks clearly evident. "I'm going to take this home, and peel off the bark, and draw a beaver on it with a felt pen so that I can have something to remind me of this hike."

Everyone looked around for short pieces of wood that a beaver had gnawed. Carol found some beaver tracks. They weren't too clear, especially since their own footprints were all over. But they found a few that were distinct enough to try casting.

"Let's go see if we can figure out how fast the river's flowing while we wait for the plaster to set," said Lynn. "My watch has a second hand on it, so it should be easy."

"O.K.," replied Melanie. "I think my pace is about 2/3 of a metre. If I take fifty paces downstream, that'll be about 35 metres. You stand here with your watch. When I've gone fifty paces I'll holler, and somebody can start floating something down the river. Make it something easy for me to spot when it passes by."

"Here's an old dead teasel," said Jenny, breaking off the weed. "If I can tie it to this stick with some old long grass, will that do?"

"It might. We can try it," said Melanie, setting off down the river's edge. She did her best to keep her paces evenly spaced, not always easy with hummocks of grass and rocks in her way. "Forty-nine, fifty . . . I'm here!" she yelled back. "Float the ship!"

The current of the river, still swollen from the spring flooding, carried the teasel-decorated stick swiftly down.

"Time!" shouted Melanie as the stick passed her.

"Twenty-five seconds," Lynn called back.

When Melanie returned to the starting point, the others were scratching in the mud, trying to figure out how many kilometres an hour the stick was travelling. Finally Lynn straightened up and said, "I keep getting confused, but I think it's around five and a half kilometres an hour. Remember last year, Melanie, when we hiked down the other side of the river and there was this little peninsula where we decided to cook lunch?"

"Do I ever!" said Melanie. "You thought it would be a good

idea to throw your shoes across to the end of the peninsula and then wade across to get them. Only you didn't know your own strength and one shoe ended up on the other side of the point and went sailing down the river. Was it ever funny!"

"Did you get it back?" asked one of the girls.

"No way! That river was flowing so fast and it was deeper than it is now and I wasn't taking any chances of it carrying me down too. It was the end of a good pair of shoes. Well, they weren't so good, but my mum wasn't very happy about it. The hike before that I'd lost a sweater. Heather was our P.L. then, and she said she'd never take me hiking again unless I either smartened up or got a more sympathetic mother!"

"So which did you do?"

"Both! After my mum got over being mad about my shoe (she can never stay mad long anyhow), she started telling me about some even worse things that had happened to her. Like when I was a baby and we camped across Canada, and she left our tent poles behind at a campsite and they didn't discover it until five hundred kilometres later.

"But I smartened up too, didn't I, Mel?"

Melanie looked doubtful. "I guess so. That's why we elected you P.L., anyhow. Or else we thought you needed taking care of, and if you were supposed to be our fearless leader, it might be better for you too!" She ducked when Lynn threw a handful of muddy river water at her.

They inspected the plaster casts of the raccoon tracks, but found they were still too soft to lift.

"I know what we can do," said Lynn. "Let's play the listening game. Who knows, we might even hear a beaver slap its tail! We split into two teams, one on each side of the creek. Then we all find a spot and sit absolutely still for five minutes and listen. We try to remember everything we hear, and see which team hears the most things. If you can't identify the sound, you have to be able to imitate it. O.K.?"

Jenny, Carol, Melanie and Kim went to the other side of Mud Creek, and found themselves comfortable spots to sit. Then they waited for Lynn to make her loon call, which would signal the start of the five-minute silence. She did it by cupping her hands over her mouth in a special way and blowing. Nobody but Lynn's family knew how to do it. After the eerie call, a deep quiet fell.

Jenny wriggled. Sticks crackled underneath her and Melanie glared at her. Keeping that still was hard. Something — a faint honk — made her look up. Far up in the sky appeared a fast-flying V-formation of geese, northward bound. Closer sounds became apparent. The burbling of the river, the wind disturbing a winter-broken branch, a chirp of an unseen bird. A caterpillar crept along a log nearby but Jenny couldn't even imagine a sound from its gentle motion. The loudest sound around was her own breathing. Then an abrupt rat-a-tat-tat made her jump. It sounded as if someone were knocking on a door.

Lynn's loon call came sharply through the air. The two groups got together and told each other what they'd heard.

"That woodpecker scared me," said one. "I thought it was right on my head, then I spotted it about five trees away."

"Weren't the geese super? Last November I saw a flock of Canada geese flying south. Wouldn't it be funny if these were the same ones? I wonder how they find their way."

"Did anyone hear the thunder?" asked Melanie. "Just before you called, Lynn, I heard a rumble far away. It sure sounded like thunder."

The sky, which had been blue and peaceful when they had first reached Mud Creek, now had fast-moving clouds in the west. Edged with black, they looked ominous.

"Let's go get the track casts and pack them away," said Lynn. "I don't want them to get wrecked after finding such good ones."

The plaster was almost dry, certainly hard enough to be packed carefully between facial tissues in the empty plastic containers Lynn had brought for the purpose.

"Before we start, let's make sure everyone has her raincoat at the top of her knapsack so that it's handy to get if it rains."

Lori, who hadn't brought a knapsack, was also without a raincoat. "What'll I do?" she asked. "I didn't think we'd ever need a raincoat. Anyhow, I don't have a real raincoat. My mother always drives me if I have to go somewhere in the rain."

Lynn and Melanie exchanged glances. "I told you all to be sure and bring a raincoat," said Lynn, looking very annoyed. "You helped make the list of what we needed for the hike at Guides last week." She felt like saying something nasty.

A roll of thunder, closer than the one they had heard earlier, brought tears to Lori's eyes.

"Anyhow, I'm — I'm . . . " she faltered. Looking at Lynn's angry face, she couldn't bring herself to admit that she was afraid of thunderstorms. Lynn didn't seem to be frightened of anything, and that made Lori feel worse.

"You're what?" demanded Lynn, who had a pretty sure idea of what Lori was about to say. The other girls were standing around, knowing that Lynn was justifiably annoyed over Lori's failure to have brought rainwear. At least she could have let Lynn know ahead of time, and they could have borrowed a raincoat. But they felt very uncomfortable because they felt sorry for Lori, who was obviously more upset by the thought of the approaching storm than by Lynn's annoyance.

Melanie reached in the side pocket of her knapsack. "Look," she said, "here's something that will help keep Lori dry if it rains. I can cut holes for her head and arms in this plastic garbage bag and she can wear it."

"I'm glad one of you is prepared," said Lynn, wishing she had thought of it first. She was beginning to feel sorry that she had jumped on Lori so hard. She searched her mind for a way to make up for it. "Lori, I'll put the garbage bag on top of my knapsack and you stay close to me. Then if it does rain — and it sure looks like it's gonna — we can pop it over your head fast."

She hoisted her pack frame onto her back and beckoned everyone. "C'mon you guys, let's get going. No use standing here just waiting for it to rain!"

The clouds were rolling up faster now, and most of the blue sky was disappearing into smaller and smaller patches. A kildeer called at the water's edge and flew across in front of them. The thunder was louder and more frequent. Occasionally a wild gust of wind struck them chillingly.

A sudden thunderclap, louder than any of the others, made them all jump. Huge raindrops began to fall, slowly at first, then with a speed that made everyone don raincoats quickly.

Lynn pulled the plastic bag over Lori's head and shoulders. "It won't do much for your arms, but otherwise it looks like a pretty good raincoat." She felt Lori shivering. It wasn't that cold. "Lori, it's only a thunderstorm. I've been caught in them lots of times and I've always survived. It won't hurt you."

Lori's eyes were filled with worry. "I hate thunder. So does my mother. She wouldn't have let me come if she'd known the weather was going to be like this!"

Carol was walking close behind, listening. "I don't like thunder either, Lori," she said. "When I was little we saw some trees near our cottage get hit by lightning. They split right down the middle."

"That's a dumb thing to tell her when she's scared already," said Lynn, turning to give Carol a black look. The effect was somewhat spoiled by a large raindrop falling from her nose to her chin. "Can't you think of something more cheerful?"

"Well, it's true," said Carol. "Lightning does hit trees. And it even hits . . . "

"Something every time it flashes," interrupted Melanie. "Mostly it hits the ground and that's that. Let's not be silly. We all walk to school every day and if we stopped to think about it, we could get ourselves all worked up about being hit by a car. More people are hit by cars than by lightning. If you spent your time worrying about such things, you'd never stir from your own house."

"Oh yes, you would," rejoined Lynn. "I read that more accidents happen in kitchens than anywhere else. That's not even counting cooking accidents — like the time I made chocolate chip cookies with two cups of salt instead of sugar. You should have seen them. They positively glistened! We had to throw them all out. My brother ate a few. He'll eat almost anything. But not those!"

The rain was still coming down hard, and the ground underfoot was spongy and squishy. Ahead of them they could just make out the outline of the bridge at the highway where they would turn for the shortcut back to town. The thunder had almost stopped. Walking in the rain had become easier, and their feet had accustomed themselves to a new rhythm.

"This is really fun," said Jenny to Carol. "I've never walked so far in the rain before. I'm glad the thunder's going away, though. I'm not really afraid of it, but I'd just as soon watch that kind of storm from inside the house. Even Lori's having a good time now, by the look of it. I'm glad Lynn didn't get really mad at her. It would've spoiled everything."

"Me too. Lynn's pretty good most of the time. She gets impatient, but she always ends up trying to help you. Listen, she's trying to say something to us."

Lynn had stopped and was wiping the rain off her face with the back of her hand. "Why don't we sing? Let's see how many songs it takes us to get to the bridge. What'll we begin with?"

"How about 'Green Grow the Rushes-ho'?" suggested Melanie. It's good and long."

Five verses later, Carol suddenly stopped singing and grabbed Jenny's arm.

"Sh-h-h, I hear something. Listen!"

As the voices died away, they heard someone calling for help. For some time, their view of the river had been obscured by the thick growth of trees and the high bank. The voice was coming from the direction of the river. The girls made their way down the slippery sides of the wet slope, and were horrified to see two young boys clinging to a raft a little way out in the river. It seemed to be partly caught on something. An old willow tree hung out over the river, its long tentacles of branches tantalizingly close to the grasp of one boy. The other boy didn't seem to be trying to help at all. He just sat on the raft hugging one of his legs.

"Look for a long stick — a strong one," shouted Lynn. Then she called to the boys. "It's all right. We'll help you. Just stay still and don't tip the raft over."

Melanie had a long stick in her hands, but when she tested it, it snapped in two. "This is no good. Jenny, reach into my knapsack for my hatchet and I'll cut off this low branch."

In seconds, Jenny had the hatchet out and Melanie chopped a long, sturdy branch. Meanwhile, Lynn had taken a long piece of rope from her pack and tied a loop at one end.

"Boys," she called, "if I can throw this rope to you, can you put the loop round a board on your raft, and maybe tie it further along too? We'll hold the stick out to you, and you can help pole the raft in while we pull on the rope."

It took several throws before the boy was able to catch the rope, despite the accuracy of Lynn's throwing. He was afraid to reach out too far lest the raft tip, and it seemed to be floating further away from shore. Finally he caught it, slipped the loop over the end of a board and attached the rope to another board as well. Several girls held on to the other end of the rope as firmly as they could, although keeping a footing on the wet ground was difficult. Melanie had slipped off her shoes and socks, rolled up her jeans, and gone into the water as far as she dared, holding the branch in front of her and towards the raft.

The boy grabbed the branch and as Lynn and Carol pulled on the rope, he helped guide the raft to the river's edge. The other boy had scarcely moved.

"Be careful of Donnie," warned the boy as he clambered off the raft. "He's my cousin and he hurt his leg. He's scared to walk."

In a short time the girls had the raft on land, with Donnie still sitting on it, his teeth chattering and tears rolling down his face. Melanie got out some ground sheets and with the help of Kim and Carol, was rigging up a shelter of sorts. It seemed a bit silly, when they were all so wet anyway, but it was easier to work when the rain wasn't pouring straight on them all the time.

The boy, whose name was Chris, told how he and Donnie had been trying out the raft they had built when the storm had come up. They had started for shore quickly, but while pulling the raft up to safety, Donnie had tripped over tree roots and done something to his leg. Chris had wanted to go to a farm for help, but Donnie had begged him not to leave him alone in the storm. That's when they had decided to try to go down the river on the raft, despite the storm. That way they could stay together, Donnie wouldn't have to walk, and they were sure they could attract a motorist's attention when they neared the bridge.

"Wow, what a chance to take," said Lynn. "It wouldn't have taken you long to go to a farm for help. You both could've drowned."

"I know," said Chris. "But he was so scared, I couldn't leave him. It was the only thing I could think of to do. When I heard you guys singing and I could sorta see you through the trees, I started to yell. I thought you'd never hear me — you sing so loud!"

When they looked at Donnie's leg, they found he had a nasty graze and a bad gash which had bled a lot. He had a blood-stained mitt in his pocket which he had held against it not realizing that, dirty as it was, it had helped stop the bleeding.

Jenny and Lori volunteered to go ahead to try and phone Donnie's parents from the closest farmhouse on the highway. Lori seemed really anxious to help. The rest were going to take turns carrying Donnie, using a four-handed lift, after they had looked after his leg.

"How old are you, Donnie?" asked Melanie. She was washing around the wound gently, avoiding any danger of it bleeding

again. It could be cleaned up properly when they got him home. She dabbed some antiseptic on it, then bandaged it. Lynn took off his sodden windbreaker, and put the extra sweater she had brought on him. Then she created another garbage-bag raincoat to keep him dry.

"Eight," Donnie answered. "My birthday was yesterday. That's how come I was staying overnight at Chris's place."

"We built the raft with a hammer I gave him for his birthday," added Chris. "It's lucky it's him and not me. I weigh a lot more'n him and I bet you couldn't carry me. What are we gonna do about our raft?"

"It's well up on the bank here," said Lynn. "Maybe your dad will let you come back and get it sometime." "If he has any sense, he won't," she thought. Anyone who let two small boys go rafting on the river in April couldn't be too bright.

"I don't think so," said Chris doubtfully. "He doesn't even know we made it. Nobody knows we came down to the river."

Despite Donnie's small size, he was a heavy load to carry. They didn't like to change carriers too often, because he was still rather tearful and complained that his leg hurt. As they neared the bridge, they saw Jenny and Lori coming towards them with big smiles on their faces.

"My mum's here," shouted Lori. "She was waiting in the car beside the bridge. She thought we'd turn up there sooner or later and she was worried about — well, she's here, and she'll take Donnie and Chris home."

"That's terrific," said Lynn. "You better go with them, Lori."

"Oh no," said Lori. "I already told her I was walking all the way. I can't get much wetter."

Mrs. Marsh, Lori's Mother, helped Donnie into the car. "Lori says that none of you will want a ride into town. Are you sure?" she asked.

Lynn looked at the rest for confirmation of her decision. "That's right. We're all wet and dirty anyhow, and it's only a mile from here. If you're sure you can manage with the boys without one of us to help, we'd just as soon walk."

"And we haven't quite eaten all the food yet, Mrs. Marsh," added Melanie.

"We haven't?" said Lynn. "What haven't we . . . ? My gorp! We haven't had my gorp yet, and it's the gorpiest gorp I've ever made." She dug into the depths of the long side pocket of her pack and gave everyone a small waxed-paper twist. "Let's go!"

As Mrs. Marsh passed them in the car, she watched their happy faces in the rear-vision mirror. The words of the song they were singing made her smile.

"We are Guides, all Guides, and in unexpected places you'll see our friendly faces . . . "

INBETWEEN 4

WITH A PACK ON YOUR BACK

Hiking, in the open air, with a pack on your back, can give you a feeling of freedom and adventure such as you may never have known. A backpacking trip, carrying your 'home' on your back, can lead you to places where no car could ever take you. Finding what's around the next corner, over the next hill, beyond the tallest tree, will let you know what it must have been like for the first people who explored this vast and varied land of Canada.

Your Pack

Even if you can't afford to buy a pack, you can make one to use until you have saved enough money to buy a better one. An old pair of jeans or an old pillowcase can be turned into a useable pack. Look at the pictures and see if you can make a pack.

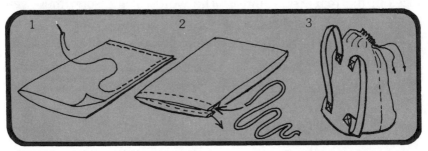

Perhaps you can design a better one yourself. Lined with a plastic bag, it's even waterproof. Sew foam rubber under the shoulder straps for comfort.

Whether you make or buy a pack, be sure to try it on before hiking, or before buying. Put something in it to get the feel of a loaded pack on your back and walk around. Check the seams and closing to make sure they are sturdy.

A pack frame makes a pack much easier to carry. One made of tubular aluminum is very light. The shoulder straps should be wide, padded, and attached level with the top of your shoulders. The pack shouldn't be able to swing, but should be firmly attached to the frame, so that it almost seems like an extension of your body. A good pack frame for heavy loads has a wide waist strap attached below the waist.

THE CORRECT WAY TO CARRY A PACK

Your pack should be carried high on your back, *with the heaviest items at the top.* You should be able to walk upright, not bent over. If you have ever watched hikers at the end of a long hike, you will remember that the most tired ones are those who hike leaning forward. A properly designed, and correctly loaded pack lets you walk straight and almost effortlessly.

Packs with outside pockets are much more useful than those with only one compartment. These give easy access to frequently needed items.

If you are backpacking overnight, you will need a sleeping bag. Attach it at the bottom of your frame or put it in the bottom of your pack. You may want a small, lightweight tent, or a tarp that you can rig up to trees with strong, light rope. A sheet of heavy-gauge plastic makes a good shelter.

Plastic bags or cotton drawstring bags keep items clean and separate. A good hiker never has a loose jumble of stuff in her pack. Avoid breakables like glass jars. Don't take more of anything than you expect to use. Save small plastic containers to pack the right amount of food. If you use plastic bags in which to pack food, use a double bag. If the outer one gets a hole in it, the inner one will prevent leakage.

Survival Kit

What would you carry with you on any hike?

first aid kit	*knife*	*flashlight*
matches (waterproofed)	*rope*	*candle stub*
some energy-giving food	*compass*	*map*
pencil and paper	*piece of plastic*	*whistle*

What would you add? What difference would it make it it were summer, winter, on a boat, on a snowmobile, on a bicycle?

Have you ever made up your own personal survival kit? How compact and lightweight can you make it and still have it useful?

BEFORE YOU GO ON A PATROL HIKE, REMEMBER...

(i)   to tell your Guider and your parents where you are going and when you expect to come back.

(ii)   the Hiking Rules which you'll find in *Policy, Organization and Rules*, sections 829-830.

(iii) to take along your personal 'survival kit'.

What to do if you're lost

(i)   Keep calm. If you panic, you won't be able to think clearly.

(ii)   Check the resources of your group. Find out what equipment and food you have, and plan how to use them.

(iii) Don't wander around aimlessly. If you have told someone where you were going, and you think you are really lost, the best thing is to stay right where you are so that searchers can find you.

(iv)   If you think you might have a prolonged stay, look around for a safe place to light a fire, and material to build a shelter if you have to stay overnight. Keep the group together. Don't wander around in the dark.

(v)   If you do decide to try to find your way, look for signs of civilization, like power or telephone poles, and follow them. Going downhill often leads you to a river or lake, which may mean a trail is nearby.

(vi)   If you need a distress signal, and have a safe place to build a fire, build three fires in a triangle. (Three anything is a distress signal.) If you add green boughs to your fires, they will send up a dense smoke which might be spotted by a fire patrol.

(vii) In the summer, make sure you have insect repellent with you. In the winter make sure you have lots of warm clothing. Read the page on Hypothermia (page 341).

(viii) If you haven't a compass, remember the sun will tell you approximate directions, if you know what time of day it is.

Use your head to save your feet

This old saying will help keep you comfortable while hiking. Your feet (the earliest means of transportation!) are essential to hiking, so if you know how to keep them in good condition you will be able to hike many miles — or kilometres. Here are some common-sense tips (a Guide is not a fool, remember?)

(i) Sturdy, well-fitting shoes are a must. Hiking boots are even better. They should be large enough that heavy socks, or two pair of lighter socks, can be worn. Never go hiking in new shoes. Break them in first, by wearing them for a while at home.

(ii) Good wool socks are most comfortable. Many people prefer two pair of socks. If your socks have holes, leave them at home. New, or almost new, socks are best. A good hiker carries extra socks. A change of socks in mid-hike may save you from sore feet, or even blisters, later.

(iii) In cold weather, if your feet are cold the rest of you is more apt to feel cold. As well as wearing warm socks you should keep your body warm with suitable clothing. Any excess heat from your body goes first to your fingers and toes.

(iv) Moleskin patches (available in most shoe stores and drugstores) should be carried, and applied immediately if sore spots are felt on the feet. A piece of plain adhesive tape will also serve to help prevent blisters.

(v)   Before you put on your socks, put a dusting of talcum powder on your feet.

(vi)   Rubber boots make for uncomfortable hiking after a short time. Avoid wearing them for other than short distances.

(vii) Try some foot-strengthening exercises. (You can even do these while you watch television!)

—Stand on a book and curl your toes over the edge.

—Pick up small objects with your toes.

—Roll your arches (one at a time) back and forth over a bottle, while you wiggle your toes.

—Stretch your legs straight out in front of you, and slowly rotate your feet keeping the toes curled under. Go inwards and outwards.

—Do deep knee bends slowly.

—Lie on your back, prop up your bottom, and bicycle. (This gives you an upside-down view of the television set.)

There's a Blackfoot Indian legend about feet. An Indian, being chased by his enemy, found that his feet were slowing down. The Indian said, "Feet, if you don't help me, I shall be killed." His feet replied, "Don't talk to us; talk to your head. You always take good care of your head, putting oils on it several times a day, but you never do anything for us." The Indian then said, "O feet, if I am killed, my enemy will take my scalp-lock and put it in an honoured place, but you he will only chop off and feed to the dogs." His feet then woke up and carried him swiftly to safety. And that is why the Indians massaged their feet and warmed them in front of the campfire before going to bed.

A first aid kit for your hike

Do you have a first aid kit that you can put in your pocket or pack whenever you go hiking? If you use up something in it, do you replace it immediately, so that it's always ready to go? If not, now's the time to make up your own first aid kit.

First, you will need a waterproof container that will close tightly. Look for metal or plastic containers. Pipe tobacco often comes in suitable tins (washed out before you use them), so if your father smokes a pipe, you might give him a suitable tin of tobacco as a gift and hope for the tin later!

Next, think of different kinds of accidents that might happen on a hike and what you would need to treat the injury. Make a list of both, and you will soon know what you need in your first aid kit. Here's a list of possible injuries and of items that would help.

INJURY	FIRST AID EQUIPMENT
Sliver	Tweezers, or sharp needle with match to sterilize it.
Scratches and small cuts	Antiseptic, adhesive gauze bandages
Insect bite	Baking soda (in small bottle or foil) to make a paste with water
Burns	Sterile water in container
Bleeding from wound	Gauze pad (or triangular bandage folded)
Injured arm or foot	Triangular bandage for arm sling or support bandage for knee, ankle or foot
Large graze	Antiseptic, gauze bandage, adhesive tape, scissors to cut the tape

TRIANGULAR SLING

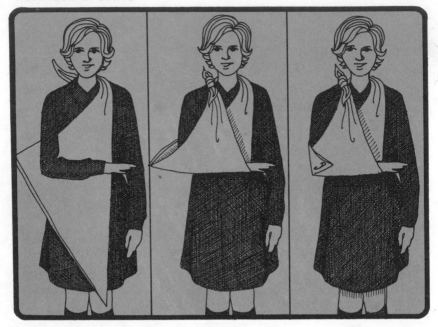

It's a good idea to tape some coins to the inner lid of your first aid kit for use at a pay telephone. A pencil stub rolled in a piece of paper might be useful. Your clothing might need emergency treatment, so a few safety pins and a threaded needle might save embarrassment if your jeans split!

Simulate wounds and practise treating them

You can simulate real wounds very easily, and practise your first aid treatment more realistically. The patient must act like a patient, and not get the giggles, or it will be hard to treat her with the care that a wound deserves. But don't scare younger girls.

Try these: Simulate frostbite by rubbing on white eye make-up.

Simulate a graze by applying a cold cream base, and rubbing in lipstick.

Simulate a person in shock by applying talcum powder.

Simulate glass in a wound by smoothing flesh coloured plasticene on skin and placing a sliver of clear, stiff plastic in it. Add blood.

Simulate a bruise by applying a thin base of cold cream and rubbing in a little blue, purple and black eye shadow.

Simulate blood with thick starch and red (or red and a little blue) food colouring.

DIGGING UP THE PAST WHERE YOU LIVE

Digging up the past is what the archeologists do. By carefully planned 'digs', they have discovered a great deal about how people lived in past centuries all over the world. In museums you will find things which existed before the time of man, like fossilized plants and animals. Or you might find them yourself in a gravel pit, a beach, or anwhere you find rock. Museums have dinosaur bones, early Roman coins, pieces of pottery used before the time of Christ, and even mummified bodies from ancient Egypt. Museums often have Indian artifacts that are very old, or things like the remains of an explorer's paddle. Sunken ships (there have been many in Canadian waters) yield a treasure of fascinating things. Pioneers' tools and clothing will tell you much about what life in Canada was like in past centuries.

You can dig too! Perhaps you live in a place where, like the girls in the story, you can dig up pioneers' kitchenware. Such garbage heaps (because that's what they were) can be discovered accidentally. Or people who live in very old farmhouses may know where 'Great-aunt Sarah buried the lamps she couldn't stand

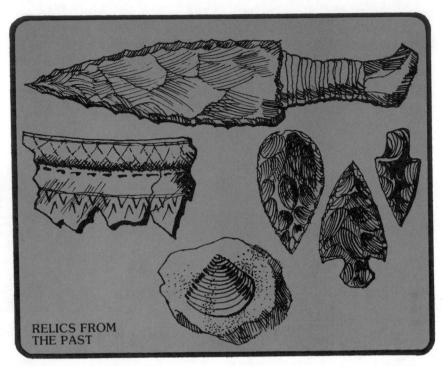

RELICS FROM
THE PAST

when she could afford new ones.' In the days before garbage collection and easy transportation to dumps, unwanted and broken articles that wouldn't burn were often left in a corner field or ploughed under the soil. Ask permission of the landowner before you dig.

Many parts of Canada have old Indian artifacts hidden in the earth. Arrowheads and other cleverly chipped implements, made by using a harder rock as a tool on a softer rock, have often been found in farmers' fields or in the earth near riverbeds.

Another way to dig up the past in your community is by asking people to share their memories with you. Make friends with some senior citizens and find out what life was like in your neighbourhood when they were young. They might even teach you things like pulling taffy, or making snow ice cream, or games new to you, or . . . ?

Can you find out...?

How your community got its name?

Where the oldest house is?

What Indians or Inuit lived closest to where you live?

Why your community was settled where it is?

How pioneer women kept house?

What people did for amusement?

If you have a local museum, and if it needs any help you could give?

How to bake bread — and how to make an outdoor oven, and use it to bake the bread?

Something about well-known women of your community in its early days?

How many different countries people in your community (or their forebears) came from?

When Guides began in your community, and if any early Guides still live there? (Perhaps you could have a 'Good Old Days' party for them.)

The year in which a woman was first elected to a political position (like town councillor) in your community?

How far back the records of churches in your community go?

Who was the first person to be buried in a cemetery near you?

If there are any folk songs that tell about your community — and learn them?

About the kinds of handicrafts in past times, and try one?

A YEAR IN THE LIFE OF A TREE

Some people think they need a leaf to identify a tree. But for more than half the year, our deciduous trees (trees which lose their leaves in autumn) are bare. Just as you are recognizable as you, with your clothes off, so trees are recognizable without their leaves. You can tell a tree by its bark, its winter buds, its flowers, its fruit (the fruit is what contains the seed), and its shape. You start with the clue you have, and with a tree book, you can find the name of the tree. Here are a lot of clues for a silver birch.

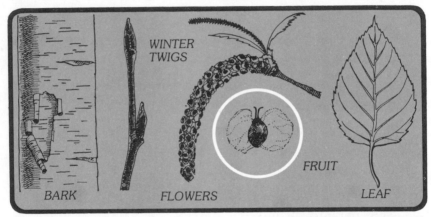

WINTER TWIGS

FRUIT

BARK FLOWERS LEAF

Here are some seasonal clues. Can you fill in the rest and identify the trees?

AUTUMN FRUIT

SPRING LEAF SPRING FRUIT WINTER TWIG

Coniferous (cone-bearing) trees — which we often call 'evergreen' — are fully clothed all year round, which makes them much easier to identify. Only the lovely tamarack, or larch, of all our coniferous trees, loses its needles in the fall. In the spring it is covered with soft, pale green needles, which become sharp and stiff in a few weeks.

Canada also has one broad-leaved tree which is green all year round. If you live near the Georgia Straits in British Columbia you probably know the arbutus tree.

YOUR KNIFE

A knife is very useful. Learn how to use it properly and treat it carefully.

— Keep it clean. Oil the joints occasionally.

— Keep it dry. Don't let it sit on wet ground. Make sure it's dry before closing it. Don't put the blade in the fire. It loses its hardness.

— Keep it closed unless it's in use. If you have a sheath knife, keep it sheathed when you're not using it.

— Make sure it's sharp. A dull knife slips and cuts the user because it glances off the wood.

To sharpen your knife: you need a sharpening stone. Lay the sharp edge of the knife blade on the stone and raise the back edge slightly. Stroke the full length of the sharp edge, from the heel to the point, across the stone; or move it in a circular motion with the pressure away from the edge. After doing this several times, turn the blade over and repeat on the other side. Continue until the edge is sharp.

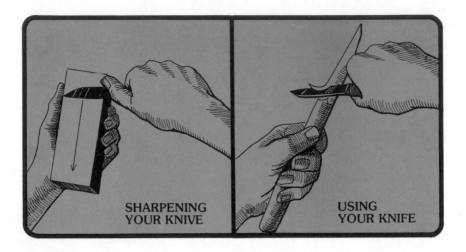

SHARPENING
YOUR KNIVE

USING
YOUR KNIFE

To use a knife: Whittle with the blade moving away from you. Make a point on a stick by digging the blade in as you whittle down towards the end of the stick. Turn the stick to centre your point.

When cutting a stick, always make diagonal cuts.

USING AN AXE OR HATCHET

These are dangerous tools if not used properly. Before trying to use an axe or a hatchet, you should receive instruction in their use from someone who is an expert. They must be kept sharp. A sharp axe or hatchet is much safer than a dull one because it will do its work properly. A hatchet is a one-handed tool and meant for light cutting. An axe is a two-handed tool, and will cut large logs.

To care for an axe or hatchet: Keep the blade sharp. Clean it with oil occasionally.

Keep the handle tight. If it loosens it may need a wedge driven in.

CARRYING AN AXE

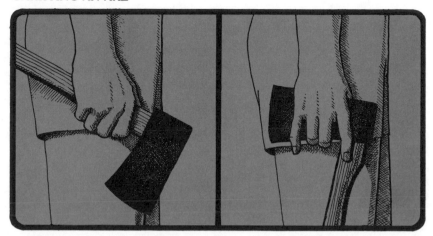

Keep a hatchet sheathed when not in use. If it hasn't a leather sheath, sink it in wood. When an axe is not in use, it should be masked in a chopping block or hung in a storage place. *Never* put the axe in the ground.

Carry an axe or hatchet by holding the handle near the head, with the cutting edge facing backwards. Alternatively, hold axehead with the handle down close to your side and the edge facing backwards.

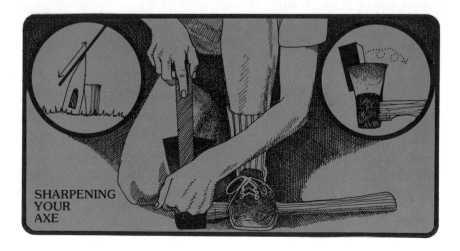

SHARPENING YOUR AXE

To sharpen a hatchet or axe: You will need a sharpening stone and a file. Keeping the axehead moistened, push the file away from the edge of the blade. File the whole edge with long, even strokes, pushing down then pulling back lightly. Work from one end to the other, slowly and carefully. When you have finished one side turn the axe over and file the other side of the blade. Finish by honing a few times on the sharpening stone in a circular motion, working from the middle outwards to both edges.

To use a hatchet or axe: Don't use brute force. It's the sharpness of the blade that does the cutting and the weight of the axehead behind it, not the amount of force you apply.

Always chop wood on wood, that is, lay the log you want to cut or split on another piece of wood, or chopping block. Never chop directly on the ground. That will damage your axe, or you.

If you are splitting wood, use the contact method. Drive the axe into the wood where you want it to split, so that it grips. Then raise the axe and the wood together and bring both of them down at the same time against the chopping block.

When cutting a log in two, use a V-shaped cut.

When lopping branches off a fallen tree or large branch, start from the bottom of the limb and work upwards, cutting the branches from the underside.

Never use an axe or hatchet if you are wearing sandals or canvas shoes. Leather offers some protection to your foot if the axe should slip. Bare feet or running shoes do not.

Make sure other people are well out of your way before you start using an axe.

If you are tired, rest. When you're tired, you have less control.

USING THE AXE

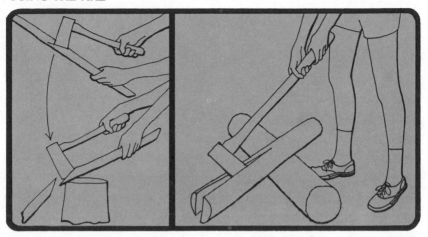

USING A SAW

There are many kinds of saws, including some light-weight, collapsible saws which are sold for backpackers. For sawing firewood into suitable lengths, a Swede saw or two-handled saw is probably the most useful.

The main points to remember in sawing wood are not to use much force (again it's the blade that does the work, not your push) and to saw in a steady rhythm. Find an expert to show you how and help you practise.

WHAT CARE WE FOR WIND OR FOR WEATHER?

Do you know the lovely song in the *Jubilee Song Book*, called 'Gypsy Lad', that begins "What care we for wind or for weather who crouch 'round the campfire?" The words and the tune fit the hiker's light-hearted feeling exactly. But even the most carefree hiker likes to know what the weather is apt to be like.

We all know that even the official weatherman can be mistaken in his predictions. But, because he knows the signs and how to read them and has all sorts of accurate equipment like observation satellites, radar, and complex measuring devices to help him, the meteorologist is more often right than wrong.

Long before there were scientific instruments, people made weather forecasts. Some of the means they used have proved to be very inaccurate, but some are good signs of coming weather. Test these against your own experience. Keep a record and see how often they are right.

"Red sky at night, sailor's delight;" (i.e. good weather next day)

"Red sky in the morning, sailor's warning." (poor weather)

"A ring around the moon means rain is on the way."

"Rain before seven, clear by eleven."

"Short notice of rain, it soon is past;
If long foretold, it long will last."

If you watch the clouds you will notice many different kinds. Government weather bureaus often have coloured charts, free of charge, telling about them. Clouds tell you a lot about weather.

Watching the movement of leaves, tall grass or flags will help tell you which way the wind is blowing. In most parts of Canada, an east wind or a northeast wind, is a sign of bad weather ahead. An east wind blows *from* the east.

Lightning safety is useful to know. Thunder follows lightning (being the shock waves caused by the tremendous heat of the lightning discharge), so, if you hear the thunder, you know that flash of lightning won't hurt you! In a thunderstorm, the safest place to be is in a car or in a steel-frame building.

Avoid these in a thunderstorm: a lone tree in an open field; the overhang of a cliff; small caves; isolated, prominent objects like large boulders; boats and water; rooftops.

The girls in the story were not in the safest place but when you are caught in a thunderstorm, you do what you think best. They stayed away from the river and did not huddle under a lone tree. The lightning soon passed, although the rain continued longer, and they were quite safe.

Try making a rain gauge or a wind vane

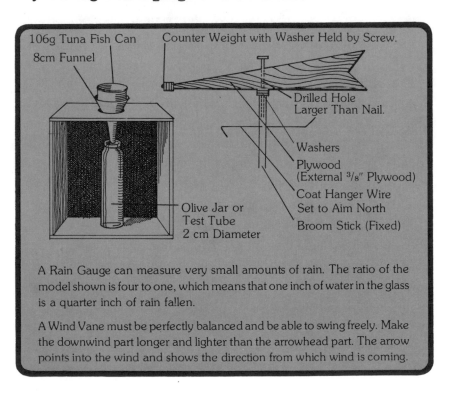

106g Tuna Fish Can
8cm Funnel
Counter Weight with Washer Held by Screw.
Drilled Hole Larger Than Nail.
Washers
Plywood (External 3/8" Plywood)
Coat Hanger Wire Set to Aim North
Broom Stick (Fixed)
Olive Jar or Test Tube 2 cm Diameter

A Rain Gauge can measure very small amounts of rain. The ratio of the model shown is four to one, which means that one inch of water in the glass is a quarter inch of rain fallen.

A Wind Vane must be perfectly balanced and be able to swing freely. Make the downwind part longer and lighter than the arrowhead part. The arrow points into the wind and shows the direction from which wind is coming.

WHERE GORP BEGAN

This is one recipe for gorp. You can think of variations for yourself. It's a high-energy, easy-to-eat food that can give you a quick lift while you're hiking.

Gorp
1 cup corn syrup, molasses or honey
3/4 cup milk powder
1 cup oatmeal
1/2 cup peanut butter
1/2 cup chocolate chips
1/2 cup wheat germ
1/2 cup (or more) crushed peanuts
1/2 cup raisins

Mix all the ingredients thoroughly. Roll into balls and wrap each in a small piece of waxed paper, twisting the ends. Chill.

The original North American gorp was pemmican, which the Plains Indians carried with them when they roamed the prairies. They made it from dried buffalo meat, pounded into a powder. They mixed this with buffalo fat and bone marrow, and often added wild berries to it. it could be eaten raw, or mixed with water, or flour and water, and boiled or fried. A small amount would satisfy a man's hunger and provide ample nutrition. In a cool climate, it kept for years.

The Indians and the Inuit were Canada's original hikers. Canada's early explorers from Europe would not have made much progress had it not been for the help of the Indians who taught them much about surviving in a harsh climate, and about the land itself. It has been said that most explorers were given 'guided tours' by the Indians!

How many things that we use today were invented and used by the native people of Canada?

— Have you ever been canoeing?

— Have you ever been snowshoeing?

— Have you enjoyed the warmth of a parka in winter?

The Indians and the Inuit are skilled with their hands. The materials they use are often those they find in nature.

— Have you ever tried making a cornhusk doll? The Indians do not put features on the doll's face. They say the child playing with it can imagine all sorts of emotions if the face is blank.

—Have you ever tried carving soapstone? The Inuit say each piece of stone has an animal or person locked inside it, and the carver merely releases what is already there.

NATIVE INVENTIONS

— Have you ever tried making moccasins?

— Have you ever tried weaving rushes, or cat-tails? Hang them to dry for a while, and then dampen them before weaving.

— Have you ever tried sewing seed beads for decoration? A good beadworker sews ten heads to the inch, closely and evenly.

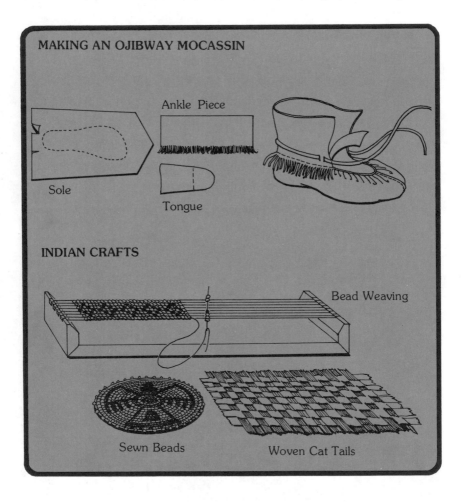

MAKING AN OJIBWAY MOCASSIN

Ankle Piece

Sole

Tongue

INDIAN CRAFTS

Bead Weaving

Sewn Beads

Woven Cat Tails

HOT DOGS ARE ONLY A BEGINNING...
TRY THESE ON YOUR HIKE!

Ground Beef Plus

Ground beef (¹/₃ lb. per person) plus whatever you want to add!
1. *Brown the ground beef thoroughly in frying pan. Drain off excess fat carefully.*
2. *Add whatever you want (within reason): chopped onion, green pepper, celery, a can of any kind of soup, cheese chunks, a small can of spaghetti, or beans, or macaroni, or corn, or tomatoes and seasoning.*

Chocolate Fondue

Chocolate chips — chunks of fresh fruit
1. *Put chocolate chips in a clean empty can. Set in a pan of hot water on the fire and melt the chips.*
2. *Spear a chunk of fruit on a fork or a stick, dip in chocolate and enjoy.*

Cheese Fondue

Cheese (your choice of variety) — unsliced bread cut in bite-size pieces.
1. *Melt the cheese; follow directions for melting chocolate above.*
2. *Spear a bread chunk with a fork or stick, dip in cheese, and enjoy.*

Twisters (also called Dampers)

Biscuit mix — milk or water (follow directions on box) honey
1. *Mix biscuit dough using a little less liquid than called for.*
2. *Twist some dough around the end of a green stick.*
3. *Hold, rotating slowly, over hot coals of fire until cooked.*
4. *Dip in honey (or butter or jam) and enjoy.*

Welsh Cakes

Biscuit mix — milk or water — 1/2 cup currants for each cup mix
1. *Mix dough and add currants. Roll out and cut into circles.*
2. *Cook over fire in dry frying pan, turning once.*

Pizza Baby

Biscuit mix as above — part of a can of tomato soup — grated
Parmesan cheese — salami or other cold meat — chopped green
pepper — chopped oregano — seasoning
1. *Mix biscuit dough and shape into a shallow 'dish' about 12 cm. across.*
2. *Spoon soup into this 'dish' and top with the other ingredients.*
3. *Place in a double wrap of heavy aluminum foil. Cook in hot coals, or on rack over hot coals close to the heat.*

Sloppy Joes (serves 3 or 4)

1 lb. ground beef — tomato or chicken gumbo soup (or both) — 1
tbsp. ketchup — 1 tsp. prepared mustard — buns.
1. *Brown the ground beef in a frying pan.*
2. *Add soup(s), ketchup and mustard. Heat through.*
3. *Serve on split hamburger buns or French bread slices.*

Apple Yummy

Large apple — 1 tbsp. brown sugar — cinnamon (or cinnamon candies)

1. *Slice apples onto a large square of doubled heavy foil, or into a buttered tart tin.*
2. *Sprinkle sugar and cinnamon on top.*
3. *Wrap securely.*
4. *Cook in hot coals about 10 minutes.*

HOW TO MAKE PLASTER CASTS OF TRACKS

You will need: Plaster of Paris, water, stirring stick, can or plastic container to mix the plaster in, cardboard 'collars' (about 5 cm. x 20 cm.) either slit as pictured or with paper clips for each collar (or you can use the bottom part of a large plastic jug for mixing, and cut the rest into rings).

Directions: Find a clear track. Place the collar around it, making sure it is fixed securely in the ground.

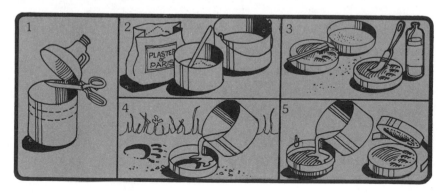

Pour into your mixing container as much water as you think will half-fill the collar. Add plaster of Paris slowly until all the water disappears. Stir until smooth. It should be fairly thick, but it should flow without being runny — something like thick cream, or melted icecream. Pour into the collar. Let set until hard, about twenty or thirty minutes, depending on the moisture in the air. Lift, and remove collar. Brush off excess dirt. When mold is thoroughly dry, you can clean it well using an old toothbrush. If you wish, you can paint the tracks to make them show up better.

What you will have is a negative impression of the tracks. If you want a positive impression (that is, indented, the way you really saw them), you have to make it from your negative.

To make a positive cast of your track, coat the negative with cooking oil. Secure a cardboard collar around it with an elastic band. Pour in a mixed batch of plaster of Paris to a depth of about 3 cm. Let it set very hard. To separate the two parts you may have to slide a knife blade between them. You can also make plaster casts of leaves and ferns. You will need some plasticene. Roll it out until it is smooth, and place the leaf or fern on top. Using a bottle or can, press the leaf carefully into the plasticene, vein side down. Remove leaf, collar the plasticene, and pour in your plaster.

You still have some plaster left?

Try pouring it into a round shape (with a collar, or into an oiled plastic container) and before it's dry, place pretty stones in a pleasing pattern. Or place the stones on the bottom before you pour the plaster. Then you can 'sink' a hanger (string loop or wire loop) on top, so that you have a plaque to hang on the wall.

Try pouring it into a partially blown balloon. As it dries, squeeze the balloon to make funny shapes. When it's dry, remove the balloon, name your animal, and paint it wild colours.

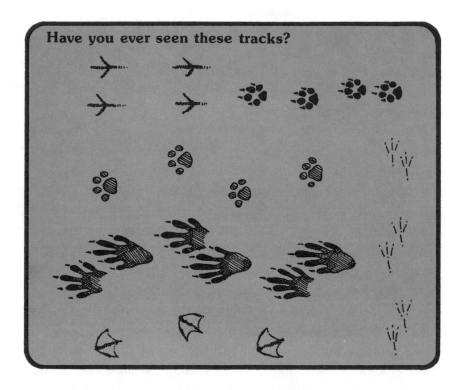

Have you ever seen these tracks?

What do your own tracks look like?

With a friend, try doing various things and see what difference it makes to your tracks if you walk, run, skip, hop, jump, carry a load (like your friend), walk backwards, or push a bicycle.

Find a place where you can carry out some of the above activities, and then ask others to deduce what you were doing.

How good a detective are you?

What can you tell about a person's weight or height from the kind of footprints she leaves?

Do you know that the Australian aborigines are the best trackers in the world? The faintest sign left behind can be spotted by their sharp eyes. They have trained themselves to be tremendously observant because their survival was often dependent upon it.

BIRD WATCHING

Wherever you live you can be a bird watcher. Of the hundreds of different kinds of birds which live in Canada for all, or part, of the year, some are near you.

The best time for bird watching is early morning. The best time of year is spring, when many birds may pass through (some to stay) in the part of Canada where you live. In autumn, when birds are winging southward again. you will also find bird watching interesting. But then their songs which were strong in the spring mating season, are quiet, and some birds' colours have changed.

There are many field guides available in libraries and bookstores which will help you identify birds by their appearance. Records of bird songs and calls are also available. Some birds, like the bob-white of the fields or the white-throated sparrow of the northern forests, are a lot easier to hear than see.

If you are fortunate enough to have a pair of binoculars, you can watch birds more closely. But the silent watcher, even without binoculars, who is willing to wait motionless for the birds to trust the quiet, is usually rewarded with the sight of many different birds.

— Have you ever seen a swallow urge its young to leave the nest, by flying close with a tasty meal of insects, daring the little birds to come out to dine?

— Have you walked on a beach and had a noisy sandpiper draw you far from its nest?

— Have you looked at a flicker hole in a tree and seen the huge young flickers and wondered how they'll ever squeeze through the hole?

— Have you ever seen a chipping sparrow, nesting in a small evergreen not far above the ground, defend its young against a marauding garter snake who fancies a meal of tasty baby sparrow?

SOME COMMON CANADIAN BIRDS

Watch but don't touch.

Have you watched birds eat? When people say 'she eats like a bird', they don't know what they're saying. Many birds eat the equivalent of their own weight, or more, each day. The contents of a woodpecker's stomach might contain thousands of ants — one hearty meal.

A bird's beak gives you a clue to its favourite food. The seed and nut eaters, like bluejays and finches, have stout, short bills for cracking open their food. The woodpeckers have long, sharp bills like chisels for boring into the bark of trees in search of larvae, and very long tongues to lap the sap and trapped insects. Flycatchers and swallows with sharp, thin beaks pluck mosquitoes and other flying nuisances out of the air in what appears to be an effortless way. Watching a heron stand motionless and suddenly spear an unwary fish, or a kingfisher dive from a telephone wire to catch his fish far below in the pond, makes human fishing with all sorts of fancy equipment seem crude.

Most bird watchers like to keep a list of the birds they have seen and identified. If you would like to start one make sure you put the date and where you saw the bird. How long do you think it will be before you have seen twelve different birds? Perhaps by the time you have finished Guides you will have seen and identified thirty or forty!

In many parts of Canada, interested people take part in a 'Christmas bird census'. Close to Christmas Day, they go to places where chances of seeing birds are good (where they can find food and water and shelter) and see how many different kinds can be seen in one day.

A banquet for the birds

In good weather, birds can and should find their own food. In the winter they appreciate the helping human. If you start in the late fall to encourage bird visitors, they will probably be your guests for the winter.

Try making bird puddings. Buy suet from the butcher. Melt it, and mix with a variety of goodies like nuts, sunflower and pumpkin seeds, oatmeal, grain, and even peanut butter. Put the mixture in a container and let it harden in the refrigerator. An egg carton makes a handy container. When the pudding is set, remove from the container and put chunks in a mesh bag (like the kind onions come in) hung from a tree, or on a tray bird feeder. A small log, with holes drilled in the sides and these stuffed with suet and seeds, makes another alluring bird banquet dish.

Once you start feeding the birds, keep it up. They come to depend on you. And if squirrels keep stealing the birds' food, figure out a method of putting the food beyond their reach — or feed them too!

It's easy to make a bird feeder and attract birds to your garden. Many bird feeders cost you nothing to make, and will give you (and the birds) much pleasure. Try one of these.

- Stuff a suet, peanut butter, nut and seed mixture in a cone to hang from a conifer tree, or stuff an empty onion bag with a "bird pudding".

- Cut most of one side out of a milk carton leaving a perch for a bird to sit on.

- Use a shallow plastic container and suspend it from a branch so that it won't tip.

- Put two large holes in a coconut, fill with wild bird seed, and hang from a branch.

Where do birds go for the winter?

Many birds migrate hundreds, or thousands, of miles to their winter homes and return to Canada each spring to nest. Until modern times, people didn't know what happened to the birds in winter. Some even thought they hid in the mud or flew to the moon!

Thanks to bird banding, radar observations and other methods, we now know pretty accurately just where birds travel. Some birds use definite flyways in great numbers. Most species have certain routes which they always follow and even have the same resting spots en route. Most migrating birds fly at night very high in sky. It takes a strong telescope to see them against the moon. A specially designed oscillator can pick up their cries.

Even so, nobody knows for certain how birds find their way over such great distances. Some seem to fly by the sun or the stars with unerring certainty. Many return to the same spot (perhaps under the eaves of your house) to nest. The Arctic tern makes an annual round trip of 22,000 miles as it moves from the Arctic to the Antarctic and back.

On these maps of the Americas, you will find some flyways marked. If you have a map of the world with the countries marked on, can you trace the flight of a bird using one of these routes? Find all the countries it would pass through. Then find out if there are Guides in those countries. If you have a copy of *Trefoil Round the World*, you can find out something about Guides in those countries.

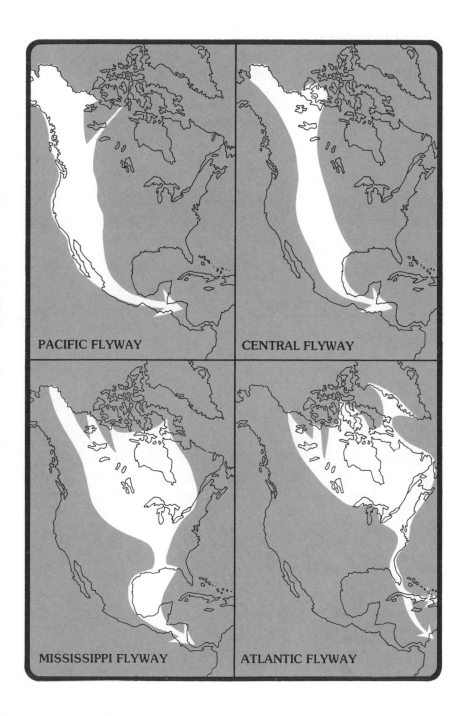

PACIFIC FLYWAY

CENTRAL FLYWAY

MISSISSIPPI FLYWAY

ATLANTIC FLYWAY

Birds I have seen

Name of bird	Description	When and where I saw it	Something interesting about it

"As a house," said Jenny contentedly, "this is just about perfect."
She leaned back against her rolled sleeping bag and gazed up at
the canvas roof above her. "Brown walls with matching ceiling
and wall-to-wall broadloom in the latest shade of grass green.
Complete with workers to build your furniture." She turned to
look at Lynn and Carol who were making something with sticks
and cord.

"Boy, do I like lazy people!" said Lynn. "You could help, you
know. When Carol and I finish lashing this stick on, you can work
on the other end of it. It's gonna be a good luggage rack. Then we
can get our suitcases up off the ground. You can go out and see
how the others are getting along with the washstand, or go and
see if they need our help yet for dinner. Our tent's Caty's Help
today."

Jenny got up slowly. "The only time you can stand seeing
someone not doing something is when you're asleep!"

"Sleep?" said Carol. "What makes you think Lynn goes to
sleep? She spends her nights thinking up things for us to do. Don't
you, Lynn? That's what Melanie told me. She said that last year at
camp you kept inventing new gadgets to make in the middle of the
night."

"That's not true," said Lynn. "Well, not quite. Just because I had this dream about a reclining chair and wakened her to tell her what a neat idea it was, she goes and exaggerates . . . where are you going, Jenny?"

"To see if they need us. Remember? You told me to."

Lori and Pam, the other two Guides in their tent, were putting the finishing touches on a lashed washstand. Around them were more tents, all being put in order. Melanie's tent had a pennant flying from the spike on the front pole. On it was the face of a wolf, teeth bared. Each camp patrol had chosen a name for itself, and they had chosen theirs for one of the earliest Guide patrols, one that had been among the Crystal Palace gate crashers.

Jenny found Mrs. Weston inside the big white tent that had shelves of food neatly arranged along its sides. She was wearing a big blue apron with 'Q.M.' embroidered on it, and below that, 'Caty'.

"Why is Caty spelled with a 'C'?" asked Jenny.

"Because it stands for 'caterer'. We used to call the Guider in charge of the food, the Q.M., short for Quartermaster. At last year's camp we started using the term 'caterer' — means much the same thing, but it doesn't sound as if you're in the army. Then 'Caty' is short for 'caterer', so you have to spell it with a 'C'. However you say it, it means food, and I guess that's good news about now, eh?"

"Sure is," agreed Jenny. "We finished that juice and cookies in nothing flat. Putting up — I mean pitching — a tent is hard work. I'm really good at pounding in pegs. What I came for is to see if you need our patrol. Lynn said we're Caty's Help today."

"I'll need some help in about ten minutes," answered Caty. "We're all going to eat together near the stores tent tonight. We've got sliced turkey, potato chips, salad and some scrumptious goodies for dessert. Instead of carting down the patrol tables, we can put ground sheets on the grass and sit around them."

"Shall I go and tell all the patrols to bring a ground sheet when they come?"

"Yes, and their dishes. But they're not to come until the dinner bell goes! Tell Lynn that I could use about three Guides in ten minutes to make the salads. And before you go back, Jenny, would you take that box of utensils and hang them on the rack near the worktable outside the tent?"

"Sure," replied Jenny. She looked around for the rack. "Do you mean this sort of branch in the ground with all the little ends of branches? It's got a big spoon hanging on it. Who made it?"

Mrs. Weston laughed. "I guess God made it. I just found it in the woods and it looked like a handy utensil rack. I sharpened the bottom and stuck it in the ground. The easiest gadget I've ever made!"

After dinner, which disappeared in short order, everyone lined up to wash her own dishes. Each of the two lines had three basins. "Hot soapy water to wash, hot clear water to rinse, and hot water with disinfectant to kill any germs," Caty had told them. Then they took their own dishes in their mesh bags back to their patrol's dining area to hang to dry.

Mrs. Mac asked the Guides to sit in a circle near the flagpole. She introduced them to the Guider with the short dark hair who had taken their health forms when they had arrived in camp. "This is Mrs. Stadnyk, who's camp nurse this week. We usually call her 'Splint'. I'm sure you've all met her little Jamie, who's three and very good at helping pitch tents." Everyone laughed as Jamie hid his head in his mother's lap. He had followed the tent-pitching procedure with great care, checking everyone's tent pegs to make sure they were in properly.

"We've got twenty-nine girls in camp, eighteen from our company and eleven from Splint's. Most of the patrols have girls from both companies so you'll soon all get to know each other. Your Patrol Leaders are going to help you make name tags for your hats tonight. As soon as I can find the bag of leather! You girls all seem much better organized than I am!

"Mrs. Bobier — most of you know her because she's tested so many of our outdoor badges — will be in later tonight. She had to go to a wedding."

"Wait'll you hear *her* camp name," said Lynn, grinning. "We call her 'Larva' at camp! The first year I camped, I was scared of bugs — any kind of bug gave me the purple heebie-jeebies. I was a real baby about it. Mrs. Bobier kept saying things like 'that's not a bug, Lynn, that's just the larva of a something-or-other', and showing me her bug book. I got so interested that I stopped being afraid and we all started calling her 'Larva'."

Melanie laughed. "When I was telling my mum about camp last year and I kept talking about 'Larva', my mum said 'My, that's an unusual name — it reminds me of something — maybe it was a name in a book I read'. When I told her what it really was she said 'poor woman; you girls are awful!' But I said it was better than being called 'Buggy'."

"The swimmers will be in tomorrow, too," said Mrs. Mac. "You know them. One's a Ranger and one's Snowy Owl in 4th Pack — Marilyn and Sue. The first thing they will be doing is testing to see who can use the boats. You have to be able to swim 90 metres and keep afloat for ten minutes. Then we can discover Treasure Island! Your Patrol Leaders will tell you about that for a bedtime story tonight."

After campfire, hot chocolate and a quick wash by the light of the moon, Lynn's tent mates snuggled down in their sleeping bags.

"What about our bedtime story, Lynn?" asked Carol. "What did Mrs. Mac mean when she said you'd tell us about Treasure Island? She had a funny smile on her face."

"It's the neatest thing that's ever happened to this camp, and I've just been bursting to tell you. You know that island in the lake? The one with the boathouse you can see from our waterfront?"

"Oh yeah," said Carol. "Somebody told me it belongs to a rich old man who never goes there. It has a haunted house or something on it."

"That's stupid. Well, it does belong to an old man who never goes there, but that's because he's crippled and can't any more. He doesn't have any children. When he did use his island, he sometimes tied his boat up at our dock. That was before I was in Guides. Sometimes the camp that was in would invite him to dinner and he would talk about what it was like here years ago. It was a lumbering area; that's why there are so few huge trees. These are mostly less than fifty years old because before that they cut them all down, and a forest fire went through part of it. He knows all kinds of interesting things, and luckily, the last time he was here, somebody tape-recorded what he said. Mrs. Mac played the tape for us when we had the camp Patrol Leaders' meeting a few weeks ago.

"He's been in a nursing home for a couple of years and won't ever be able to come back to his island. That's sad because he really loved it. He was going to sell it, but then he wondered if the Guides would like to use it. So as long as he's alive, it's ours to use, even the buildings on it. They signed a paper about it. Mrs. Mac and the Commissioner went to the city where he lives and talked to him. Sue went too. She's the Swimmer. We can use his little sailboat. It has a small motor but he doesn't think it'll work. Sue's dad's coming out to have a look at it. He's a mechanic and knows all about motors."

"Is it really called Treasure Island?" asked Jenny.

"Not really. On the map it just says Brown's Island, because he's Mr. Brown and it never had a real name of its own. We started calling it Treasure Island when Mrs. Mac told us about it. We're the first camp in this summer, so we'll be the first to explore it. I can hardly wait to see what it's like."

It was hot and sunny next morning at the waterfront, but the water itself was cold. Jenny sat on the beach rubbing her hair vigorously with a towel.

"I thought I wasn't going to make the last few metres," she said to Carol and Lynn beside her. "I just kept thinking 'Treasure Island' and that kept me going. You're both such strong swimmers. When I saw you get out of the water away ahead of me, I was really determined to finish."

"It wasn't bad," said Carol. "I've always swum in cold water. Where my grandmother's cottage is, it takes all summer to warm up. I feel sorry for the kids who aren't good swimmers. Like Lori."

Lynn looked thoughtful. "She was telling me on the way down that her mother's always afraid something awful's going to happen to her. And Lori half believes it's true. I tried to joke her out of it, but that doesn't seem to do much good. She pretends she's going along with what you say, but you can tell that underneath she's really afraid."

"I wish we could help her somehow. If she were really good at something, especially something everyone else wasn't good at, that might help," said Jenny. "Look, she's playing at the edge of the water with Jamie. Can't she swim at all?"

"A little," answered Carol. "I saw her trying in the shallow water when I got out. Won't she be allowed to go over to the island, Lynn?"

"Oh sure, she and the rest who can't swim 90 metres can go as

passengers in the camp rowboat or in Mr. Brown's boat with the motor on, if it'll go. They can't sail or canoe, though, and the weather has to be really good and the lake calm for them to go as passengers in the other boats. We have to take turns anyhow. Even counting Mr. Brown's boat, less than half of us can go at once. There are three Guide canoes and the rowboat."

"Maybe she'll learn to swim better while she's at camp. I learned to swim right in this lake at Brownie Holiday. Marilyn's really patient and she could make anyone believe she was a fish."

They drew names out of a hat to see who would be the first visitors to the island. Lynn thought the Patrol Leaders should automatically go and was a bit put out when her name wasn't among those drawn. She muttered as much to Melanie.

"When we voted on how to choose who would go first, you voted to draw names," said Melanie in surprise.

"Yeah, but I didn't think about my name not being picked. Anyhow, I didn't want to say the Patrol Leaders should be first to go. That would've sounded selfish." Lynn thought about what she'd just said. "I'm being silly aren't I? A poor sport—just when I was trying so hard not to act like that. You don't know how much I want to see that island!"

Carol and Jenny were very excited. Both their names had been drawn for the first trip. The swimmers and Splint were going with the eight girls chosen. Carol, who knew how to canoe, was in the bow of the canoe in which Marilyn was stern paddler. Jenny knelt amidships. The lake was calm, reflecting the blue sky, and only the occasional whisper of a breeze rippled the water. Within twenty minutes that had reached the island and carefully beached the canoes. They tied the rowboat to the dock, which was small and badly in need of repair. It had been painted bright red but bare wood showed through in many places.

"What a funny colour to paint a dock!" said Carol.

"Mr. Brown told us all his doors were painted red, and that we'd come to the first door first. He chuckled when he said it, so I guess this is it — the door to the island!"

Exploring the island was fun. Sue had a map which showed the outline of the island. Most of its surface was covered in green for the woods. One small black square indicated the cottage. They decided to split into two groups and each take one half of the island (on either side of the cottage) to explore.

"Do you all know what poison ivy looks like?" asked Splint. "There's a patch here. You'd better all have a good look at it, so that you can avoid walking through it if possible. After we've explored, we can all have a good wash with the cake of laundry soap I brought along. That's an almost certain way to avoid poison ivy rash if you've come in contact with the plant. It washes off the oils that cause the problem."

There were lots of footpaths to follow, considerably overgrown with grasses and wildflowers, but still fairly easy to follow. At one point, Sue's group emerged from heavy woods to face a huge boulder effectively blocking their way. A cleft down the middle had small cedars and birches growing out of it, and lichen patched most of its surface.

"Let's climb up it," said Sue.

Finding a foothold was difficult but after Sue reached the top, she leaned over and helped the rest up. The view from the top of

POISON IVY

the boulder was breath-taking. Waves lapped gently against the far side of the rock, and the lake, dotted with tiny far-off islands, stretched before them. Smaller rocks were strewn along the shore as if some great hand had carelessly tossed them there. And caught between two of them was something orange.

"Look, Sue!" exclaimed Jenny. "There's something down there. Can we go down and see what it is? We'll be careful."

They made their way down to the shore. It was hard walking until they got used to finding the flat pieces of rock quickly. They found the remains of a life jacket wedged between two rocks.

Further along the shore, where the rocks gave way to a pebbled beach, they found a small blue punt, well-weathered and somewhat battered. A short end of the painter, grey and frayed, hung limply from the bow.

"D'you think we'll find a body next?" asked Jenny anxiously.

"Somebody could've drowned and the boat washed ashore."

Carol shuddered. "I hope not. I don't want to find a body. What would we do, Sue?"

Sue was squatting beside the punt, examining it. "It looks to me as if the boat was tied up somewhere and the rope just gave way from old age. Take a look at this painter. It's worn right through. The owner had probably tied it up somewhere and in a storm, perhaps, it broke loose and got carried here."

"But the life jacket — why would there be a life jacket?"

"It was probably just left carelessly in the boat, so he lost it too."

Carol was persistent. "What if we do find a body? What'll we do?"

Sue sighed. "Phone the police from camp, of course. We'll face that problem if we come to it. Don't worry about it."

They worked their way back to the cottage by following the shoreline as much as they could. The other group was sitting on the dock, washing their legs in a pail of water.

"Hi!" called Melanie. "Did you find anything interesting? We sure did."

Carol's voice trembled slightly as she asked, "A body? Did you find a body?"

"A body! Sort of — a whole bunch of them. Baby rabbits. A little way behind the cottage is a meadow where Mr. Brown must've once had a vegetable garden. There's berry bushes and stuff, and rabbit holes. When they see you, they just sit still with their ears up, and then run like mad. Some of them are quite small and didn't know which way to run."

Carol's voice was relieved as she said, "We found an old boat washed up on the far shore, and I was sure there'd be a body too."

Sue went to the boathouse door. "Let's have a look at Mr. Brown's boat. He said it's a fourteen-foot sailboat which will be great to learn how to sail in." She wrestled with the latch and

finally managed to release the door which creaked on its rusty hinges.

"There's nothing here!" she exclaimed. "It's empty!"

Aside from an old life jacket on a hook, a couple of broken oars on a rack, some coils of rope and a winching device for raising the boat, the boathouse was indeed empty.

"I can't understand it. Mr. Brown said we'd find the boat here. The sails and sheets are supposed to be in a bag in the cottage. Let's go and check."

Sue had the key to the cottage. There were dirty dishes sitting about, and plenty of signs of bats having been there. "The bats sure didn't leave those dirty dishes," said Sue. "Mr. Brown said the place would be dusty, but otherwise in order. The sail bag isn't where he said it would be. Has anyone spotted it?"

Nobody turned it up, although they searched the small cottage thoroughly. Someone had obviously spent some time in the cottage and made no attempt to cover his traces. The fireplace was filled with ashes, and wood had been dumped in the woodbox near it. Jenny found a piece of crumpled blue paper on the wood. She smoothed it out.

"It's a cheque! Look Sue, it's made out to Melstrum's Grocery."

Sue took the cheque. "That's the grocery store in the village a couple of miles around the lake. This cheque is almost two years old. Do you know what I think? I think somebody hid out here, maybe after robbing the store. He could have used that old punt we found, then stayed for a while here, stolen Mr. Brown's boat and motor, and taken the sails while he was at it. Maybe he decided he'd have trouble cashing the cheque — it's only for fifteen dollars anyhow — and threw it in the woodbox. Let's lock up and get back to camp. The next crew over can clean up the cottage a bit."

It was suppertime when they got back and every patrol got exciting versions of the story from the girls who had been to the island. Mrs. Mac and Sue ate with Lynn's patrol and Sue outlined her theory of what might have happened.

As soon as supper was over, Mrs. Mac telephoned the nearest detachment of police. Before the dishes were done, the police car drove into camp and the policeman went down to the Guide dock with Mrs. Mac and Sue. A game had been planned, but nobody was interested until they had heard what the police had to say. Mrs. Mac gathered everyone together.

"A year ago last fall, the grocery store in the village was robbed one Saturday night. There was a fair bit of money in the till because it was hunting season. There were no witnesses, other than Mr. Melstrum himself who was alone in the store at the time.

"The robber had taken Mr. Melstrum's truck keys and stolen the truck, then abandoned it a few miles away. The police assumed he had left his own car there. It wasn't until a week later that they found out that a blue punt, belonging to one of the boys in the village, was missing. But it never turned up and nobody thought much about it, because everyone knew the boy was careless about how he tied it up and he'd said the rope was rotten.

"Weeks later, Mr. Brown's boat was found about ten miles down the lake — right at the other end — tied up, properly tied up by someone who knew what he was doing. It took a while to discover whose boat it was. When they did, the police wrote to Mr. Brown but he'd had a stroke and was in hospital, unable to understand or write back. The letter was acknowledged by a nurse who said Mr. Brown would no doubt be in contact later. But he never did get in touch with them, and our guess is that he never did hear about the theft at all."

"Where's the boat now?" asked Carol.

"As far as the police know, an old friend of Mr. Brown's has it in a barn near the village. He said he'd store it, but he's a forgetful old fellow — quite odd, in fact — and apparently no one has given it another thought. It's probably still there. The police are going to check and let us know."

"What they think," said Sue, "is that the robber holed up in Mr. Brown's cottage for a couple of days and then sailed down to the other end of the lake, probably at night, where the cottages would all be vacant, and then simply made his way to the city by bus from the highway. He would have had a lot of money in his pockets from the robbery and could easily get away."

Getting to sleep after all the excitement that day was hard. Jenny and Carol whispered long into the night until Lynn finally got them to promise not to say another word, by saying she'd tell them the best fish story they'd ever heard.

"You heard about the fish who always had his mouth open?"

"No, tell us."

"He was the one who got the hook! Now go to sleep or I'll snore in your ear, and that's a fate worse than death."

It was Thursday, and the last Guides to visit the island left as passengers in Mr. Brown's boat and Lori was among them. The boat had been found in the barn, and brought to the camp by the police. Sue had checked the motor and made a few minor repairs. The day before had been too windy for the canoes to chance the trip to the island, and too rough for the non-swimmers to go over. Sue had taken the strongest swimmers out for short sailing lessons.

All the girls who wanted to learn about sailing, even if they couldn't actually go out in the boat until their swimming had improved, had gone down to the waterfront after morning chores had been done. Many of the terms were strange to them.

"I would have thought the sails were the sheets. How come the ropes are called sheets?" asked Jenny.

"I don't know; they just are. But that's only the ones that control the sails, you know. The ones that run the sails up the mast are called halyards, just like the rope on the flagpole."

At lunch, they had great fun making up alliterative sailing names for themselves. "I'll be Jenny Jib; you be Carol Cleat, and you can be Lori Luff."

"What about me?" demanded Lynn, her mouth full of tuna sandwich.

"Lynn Leak?" said Lori shyly, and they all roared with laughter.

"And to think I was nice to you!" said Lynn sadly.

"I told you how sailing with the wind in your face was the best feeling in the world, and how great you guys were to have lunch all ready when I got back."

"Yeah," said Jenny. "You also told us that you almost pulled out the plug on the boat with your big toe!"

"Did Mrs. Mac tell you that we're going to play a wide game when the kids get back from the island later this afternoon?"

"Yes," said Lori. "She said that when we get to the island we're going to have a list of things to find and bring back. Then when we get back to our dock, there'll be some kind of instructions there. She also said that if any of us going were to do lunch dishes, we were to ask someone else to do them."

"I'll do them, Lori," said Carol quickly. "Anyhow, you helped me make the sandwiches and you didn't have to."

When the girls who had gone to the island got back to the dock later that afternoon, they found a stick planted in the sand with a ragged bit of cloth hanging at its top. Sue read the roughly written message on it aloud.

"We have captured your Patrol Leaders and hidden them. To get them back you must find the patrol flags and leave treasure from Treasure Island in their place. Then you will receive a clue to where the Patrol Leaders are. Signed, the Red-handed Gang. P.S. All your food is with the Patrol Leaders. Ha-ha. P.P.S. if you do not obey these instructions you will meet a horrible fate. P.P.P.S. If we see you, we will get you, too!"

"Well, that's easy," said Kim. "We've got the treasure in our bags here — all the things our list said to find: a round red stone, a fern that's as long as Sue's arm, a buttercup, a seagull's feather, and all the other things. So let's go get the patrol flags from the tent poles. We can boost Lori up on Sue's shoulders to reach them."

But when they got to the tents, there wasn't a patrol flag in sight. The campsite was deathly quiet with not a person around. The girls looked bewildered.

"Where are the flags? How do we know where to find them?"

"Look at that tree over there," said Lori, pointing. "There's a funny-shaped piece of paper stuck in the bark." She pulled it out. "It's either an oak leaf or . . ."

"It's a moose antler," shouted Nancy. "It's telling us something about the Moose Patrol, I bet. Maybe there are more."

It took some careful looking around, but they gradually managed to find more papers half-hidden in various places. Moose antlers, wolf tails, raccoon masks, rabbit tails, bear paws — symbols of all the patrols. As they followed the trail, the trampled grass told them more than the paper signs. When they were deep into the wooded area that surrounded the campsite, they came to a huge old charred stump, still standing as mute evidence of the forest fire a half century earlier. On its top, held down by a stone, were the patrol flags. A tape-recorder sat beside them.

"Turn it on," whispered Kim. "Maybe it'll tell us something.

Wait a minute — take the patrol flags and leave the treasure first, just in case."

Lori pushed the 'on' button. They all jumped when a fiendish laugh crackled at them. It was followed by a snarling voice.

"This is the leader of the Red-handed Gang speaking. Listen carefully. You think you're smart because you found the flags. Your troubles are just beginning! We are watching you! Look high for food, low for victims. Watch out for us. If we touch you with our evil red hands, you become helpless and join your leader in captivity."

The girls huddled together with Sue and Splint. They kept their voices as low as possible, sure that there were watching eyes and listening ears all around them. They argued about the meaning of the clue, but finally agreed that Kim's solution sounded most reasonable.

"I bet they've put something to do with supper in a tree and hidden the Patrol Leaders under the tree. They might be camouflaged with branches and hard to see, but the food might be obvious if we look up."

"But if they see us, we get caught too," said one of the girls. "We'd better not go in a big bunch. Let's separate."

"How about going in pairs?" suggested Sue. "Splint and I will each go with one of you, too. If the pairs don't stay too close together, but only keep in sight of each other, one might get caught and the other escape."

It wasn't five minutes later that Lori spotted a box of rice in the fork of a tree. She signalled to her partner and crept towards it. At the back of the base of the tree, she could see the toe of a running shoe. She had just about reached it when she heard the crackle of a branch behind her. She turned around and found herself captured by a grinning Jenny.

"Gotcha!" exclaimed Jenny triumphantly. "You have to sit here beside Lynn."

But as Jenny pushed Lori down beside Lynn, who was lying partly hidden under a brown blanket, Sue pounced out of nowhere. "Free!" she yelled. "I guess you can eat tonight, Lynn and Lori!"

It was quite a while before the other Patrol Leaders were released. Melanie never did make it. Her rescuers found themselves captured by Carol who was wearing a sweat shirt that blended in beautifully with the bush she was hiding behind.

It was a happy group of Guides who emerged from the woods an hour or so latter chattering about the game.

"The suspense was awful," said Lynn. "I was dying to go to the lat, and I knew I coudln't move! I could hear you guys coming, but I knew that Jenny was hidden nearby. That was a really neat move, Sue, when you ran to me under cover of the noise Jenny made capturing Lori."

They were busy next day preparing for Discovery Night. There were Brownies in the Holiday House and Brown Owl had asked if they could visit the Guides to see what Guide camp was like. At the Court of Honour the Patrol Leaders had talked about what Brownies might enjoy the most.

"All of us have learned so many new things this week that we could put on a sort of entertainment — skits and stuff about what we've discovered that we didn't know before."

"And we could call it Discovery Night," said Lynn. "Have you seen Lori draw? She's spent a lot of time with Larva, learning about bugs and things, and you should see the tiny, tiny pictures she draws. She can draw an ant, ant-size, and not leave out any details!"

"I know," said Larva. "She has a tremendous talent for observing detail. She sits for ages, watching an insect, and then sketches it just beautifully. Let's ask her to make an invitation for the Brownies."

"And we can end with a super campfire," said Melanie. "The Wolf Patrol is on campfire and we've been practising 'Ingonyama' and are going to tell the story about why Lord Baden-Powell was called 'The wolf who never sleeps'."

The Brownies arrived early, looking solemn and spotless. "How do they stay so clean at camp?" asked Carol, looking at her hands, blackened after scrubbing the pots. "We're not even ready yet."

"It's O.K.," said Lynn. "Mrs. Mac said they were sure to arrive early, no matter what time we made the invitation for. Sue's going to play some songs for them on her guitar. Let's get washed, so we look half decent. Anyone got a clean blouse?" She rummaged in her suitcase. "In fact, anyone got two clean blouses?"

"You did some laundry this morning, Lynn. Remember? Your clean blouses are on the clothes line. You're lucky you've got a good patrol to look after you."

It was a large circle around the campfire with the Brownies present. They weren't going to light the fire, carefully laid by the Wolf Patrol, until most of the Discovery Night activities were finished. It was easier not to have to worry about falling into the fire.

Linda, one of the Patrol Leaders from Splint's company, welcomed the Brownies. "You all know this is our Discovery Night, and we're going to tell you about things we've discovered at camp that we didn't know before. So to start off, you're all going to have a treat to eat while you watch — radish popcorn. In May, when I came to a weekend camp here with some other Guides, I helped dig the Thrift Garden near the storage building. The radishes I planted are ripe. I never planted a garden before and I never really

182

thought it'd work, but it did. I also discovered how to make popcorn over an open fire, so here's your treat. And we're glad you came. Oh yeah, you can tell which are the radishes because they're red. You can pass the bowls around now — and Brownies first."

The girls who had learned to canoe and sail put on a hilarious skit. They all pretended to be fish in the water, discussing the Guides, who were above them in boats. When the 'fish' started arguing about which bathing suit they'd go for first if a canoe tipped, Mrs. Mac laughed until the tears rolled down her cheeks.

Lynn announced Lori's discovery, because she was suddenly too shy. "Lori's discovered that she can draw insects better than the pictures in Mrs. Bobier's bug book. The first Brownie to find an insect without moving from her place can have a signed drawing of it from Lori."

In seconds, a Brownie shouted, "There's a pretty green one near me."

Lori squatted on the ground beside her and with coloured felt pens, quickly sketched a praying mantis. Then she covered the picture with clear gummed plastic, punched a hole in the corner and pinned it to the Brownie's camp hat.

There were some funny skits about cooking and even funnier ones about eating. But the highlight of the discoveries was made up by a group from Melanie's tent. They had discovered that they could create a dance to express their feelings about mosquitoes. They called it 'Mosquito Agony'. Melanie danced the part of a Guide fighting off mosquitoes while the rest, wearing long, pointed, cardboard headpieces, did battle around her. Sue strummed her guitar in accompaniment and the dancing 'mosquitoes' made appropriate buzzing sounds. It ended with the 'mosquitoes' (who all had signs on their backs saying 'Female') sinking to their death and an exhausted Melanie doing a weary victory dance in slow motion.

Jenny pulled her sweater over her head. The sun was going down and the air was a little chilly as Melanie lit the campfire. Nancy played the haunting melody of 'Rise Up, O Flame' on her recorder, and as if in obedience, a great yellow flame shot into the air.

Campfire was always special, but tonight it held an extra enchantment. The Brownies' songs, and their skits about what they thought Guides did, fitted in beautifully. The darkening sky above them, its stars growing brighter in contrast, made a perfect background for the soaring voices, singing Carol's favourite song. 'All Through the Night' had a glorious descant that gave her great pleasure every time she sang it. There was something satisfying about being able to sing a descant or an alto part.

On their way to the tent, Lori said wistfully to Carol, "I wish I could sing like you."

"I wish I could draw like you," said Carol. "That Brownie was just thrilled with her praying mantis picture."

"Drawing things is easy. You just keep looking at them and then put what you see down on the paper. But singing — even when we sing a round I can't keep with the part I'm supposed to be singing. I even plug my ears so I can't hear the rest, but it still doesn't work."

"But you shouldn't plug your ears! That's the whole thing about singing a round or singing alto or a descant. When you hear the other parts with yours, the whole sound is right. You have to hear all the parts together — something like drawing the whole praying mantis. You have to listen just as hard as you looked at that insect."

"You mean . . . something like — well, I see the whole insect first and then the separate bits of it, but I always have the whole thing in my mind even when I'm just looking at the one part I'm drawing, like the front leg."

"Yeah, I guess so," said Carol. "I've never tried drawing like you do, but that sounds like what I mean. Maybe I should try drawing with lots of looking, and you should try singing with lots of listening. Let's try tomorrow sometime, I'm too sleepy just now to sing another note!"

It was the last day of camp. Jenny looked at the pile of luggage awating the arrival of the bus. The campsite looked sad, with the tents and gadgets all gone. Even the flag, hanging limply from the pole, looked forlorn. The colour party would bring it down after Guides' Own.

"This has been such a super camp," Melanie had said, "that I wish we could have a Guides' Own right at the end of camp in the Quiet Place at the edge of the woods."

Half an hour before the bus was due, they had finished the packing and clean-up. Jenny was part of the group that had planned the Guides' Own. Carol and Lori had helped her make up a prayer that said thank you better than any of the prayers in

Mrs. Mac's books. Sue was sitting on a stump, playing her guitar as the Guides found their places on the log seats. Little Jamie had gathered daisies and put them in cans of water near the cross that someone had made by lashing two sticks together.

'Dona nobis pacem' (Give us peace), sounded over and over as more voices joined in the round. Jenny took the piece of grass she had been chewing nervously out of her mouth, cleared her throat, and began to read.

> "Lord, we've come to the Quiet Place at the
> end of our camp to say thanks for the fun
> we've had; for the new friends we've made,
> for the old friends we've gotten to know
> better and for helping everyone to put up
> with each other, even when it was hard.
>
> The weather's been perfect; good winds for
> the sailors and calm water for the non-
> sailors; sun for all of us; and thanks for
> for the rain that Mrs. Mac says every camper
> should experience, and especially for having
> the rain at night; and thanks, Lord, for
> all the beautiful things around us..."

Nancy played 'Land of the Silver Birch' on her recorder just as a breeze rustled the leaves of the trees. A white-throated sparrow joined in.

At the end of Guides' Own, they all walked over to the flagpole and sang 'Daylight Taps' as the flag was lowered for the last time.

> "Thanks and praise, for our days,
> 'Neath the sun, 'neath the stars,
> 'neath the sky,
> As we go, this we know —
> God is nigh."

A TENT — YOUR HOME AWAY FROM HOME

People lived in tents for thousands of years. In some parts of the world, tents are still made from animal hides and sewn with animal sinews, just as they were in ancient times. Until late in the 19th century when the Canadian Plains Indians could no longer hunt buffalo because the white man had caused them to be almost extinct, the familiar western teepee was made of buffalo hide. Today, most us live in tents chiefly in the summer because it's fun to live in the open air, and a tent is a handy protection from the weather.

Tents come in all shapes and sizes. Some have sewn-in floors, some are set on wooden platforms, and some have no floors. Some have poles outside, some inside, and some have no poles at all. Some are so light that they will easily fit into a knapsack; some, like marquees, are as large as a small gymnasium.

The tents most commonly used at permanent Guide camps are ridge (sometimes called wall) tents and bell tents, without floors. If you know how to pitch (put up), care for, and strike (take down) these tents, you can probably figure out how to use other kinds of tents quite easily.

With both ridge and bell tents, the basic steps are the same;

(i)   Lay the tent on the ground and put the pole(s) in place.

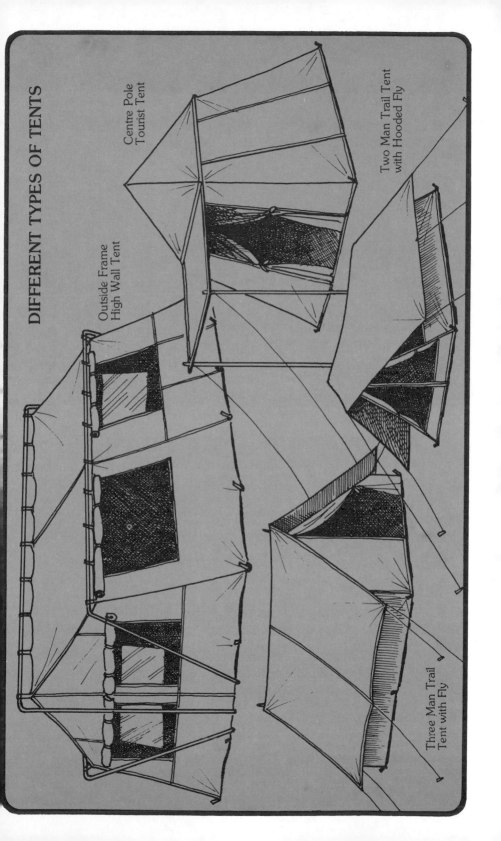

DIFFERENT TYPES OF TENTS

Outside Frame
High Wall Tent

Centre Pole
Tourist Tent

Two Man Trail Tent
with Hooded Fly

Three Man Trail
Tent with Fly

(ii) Tie the door and raise the tent.

(iii) Put the corner (figuring out the 'corners' for the round bell tent) pegs in the ground and the corner guy ropes on the pegs.

With the poles and the corner guys in place, the tent will stand. The other pegs and ropes can be put in place. You must do this properly or the tent will be lopsided and will not stand long. Improperly pitched tents also weaken the canvas.

These diagrams and instructions will help you pitch and strike your tent easily. *Except for small tents, it's not c one-person job. If everyone has a part in doing it, everyone learns together.*

Pitching a Ridge Tent

1. Choose a level, grassy spot if possible. Avoid low-lying areas where water will tend to sit. Decide where you want the door to be.

2. Lay the ridge pole on the ground on what will be the 'middle line' lengthwise of the tent. Pound in small pegs at either end as markers. Remove pole.

3. Making sure the tent door is tied, lay the bottom edge of the unfolded tent along your imaginary 'middle line', with the door at the end you want for the front.

4. Slide the ridge pole in the top (ridge) of the tent. Have two girls place the spikes on the ends of the upright poles through the holes in the ridge pole and tent. They will likely have to crawl under the canvas, and should take off their shoes.

5. The two girls holding the upright poles raise them carefully, moving the base of the poles to the marking pegs. They then stand steady, holding the poles as straight as possible, by bracing a foot against the bottom of the pole.

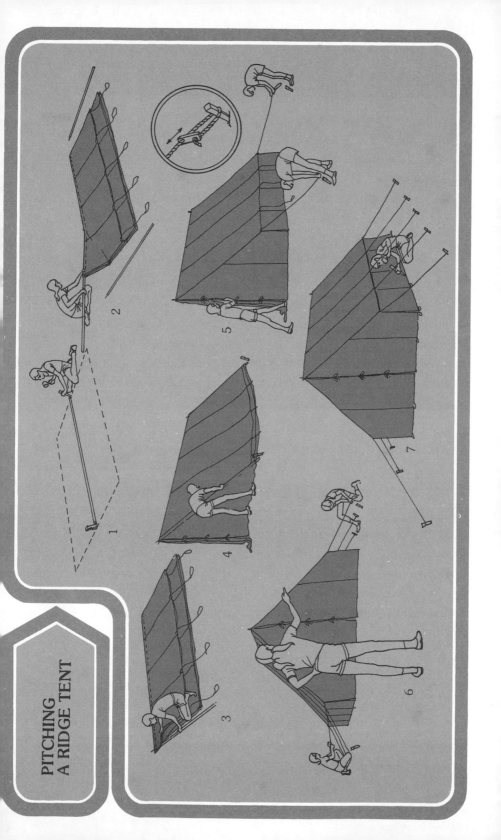

PITCHING
A RIDGE TENT

6.   Other girls pound in the four corner guy pegs, at a 45° angle facing outwards using the longest pegs for this because the corner ropes take the greatest strain. (If there is only one rope at the corner, the peg is placed at a 45° angle from the corner. If there are two ropes, two pegs are placed each at 90° from the corner.) Slip the ropes over the pegs and tighten from both sides at the same time for an even pull. The girls holding the uprights can leave them to stand alone.

7.   It's a good idea to stand at the front pole and 'sight' the poles. You should see only one upright if they are properly aligned.

8.   Pound in the side pegs and put the ropes on, again tightening both sides at once. The peg, guy rope and usually the tent seam should be in a straight line and the row of pegs from front to back should also make a straight line. This is called 'setting' a ridge tent. It's a good idea to have one girl to 'sight' for you as you decide where the peg should go.

9.   Put in the short brailing pegs at the bottom of the tent walls and slip the brailing loops over them. The brailing pegs should be facing outwards at an angle.

10.   Your tent is now pitched and ready for its occupants!

Striking a Ridge Tent

The general procedure for tent striking is to do in reverse order what you did to pitch it. See if you can figure this out for yourself before checking the step-by-step instructions which follow.

1.   Remove the brailing pegs. As pegs are removed they should be scraped free of dirt, using a stick or another peg, and laid in a crisscross pile to dry thoroughly.

2.   Remove all ropes except the four corners. Clean and stack pegs. Slide rope runner to where the rope is attached to tent. Tie the rope in an overhand knot, doubling the rope first if it's long.

3. Tie the door.

4. Have a girl outside the tent holding each upright pole.

5. Remove corner guy ropes and tie.

6. The girls who are holding the uprights slowly lower the tent to the ground, with the wind. Remove the poles.

7. Smooth the tent until it is free of wrinkles. It helps to have some girls at the corners to pull the tent taut as you do this. Sweep off any leaves, dirt or grass and continue sweeping each time you fold the tent. (You should be able to do this without standing on the tent, but if it's absolutely necessary to stand on canvas, remove your shoes and be very careful.)

8. Fold in the ropes, the ends, and the walls. You now have a large rectangle.

9. How you finish folding the tent depends on how it is to be stored. Some tents have bags and have to be folded or rolled to fit them. Check with someone how it should be done on your campsite.

10. Tie the poles together. An excellent method is to use the pole hitch. It's easy to tie and untie, and holds the poles tightly. Make an 'S' in the middle of a length of cord. Lay the poles on top of the 'S' as shown. Put the opposite ends of the cord through the curves of the 'S'. Pull tightly and tie the ends in a bow.

Pitching a Bell Tent

1. Choose your site and which way you want the door to face. Place a marker peg 'A' where you want the centre of the tent.

2. Lay the pole on the ground, with one end at the centre marker 'A', and the other at the door. Put a marker peg 'B' at the door end of the pole.

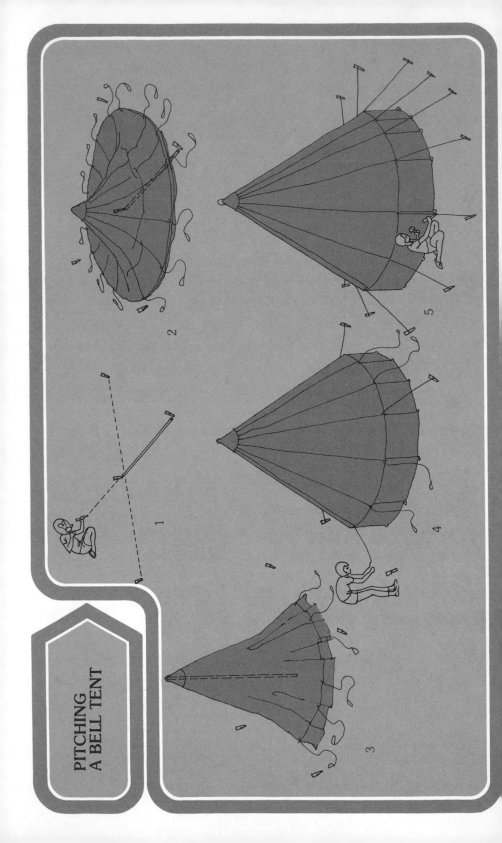

PITCHING
A BELL TENT

3.   Place marking pegs at points 'C', 'D', and 'E' in the diagram (something like 12, 3, 6 and 9 o'clock on a clock dial). These are your 'corners'.

4.   Pound in the four longest pegs at these points — 'B', 'C', 'D', and 'E' — at a 45° angle, facing outwards. Figure out which are the tent's 'corner' guy ropes by counting all the ropes (except the door), and dividing by four. It's a good idea to mark the corner guy runners with paint, so that you don't have to count the ropes each time you pitch the tent.

5.   Unfold the tent and lay it on the ground, with the eaves at the centre marking peg 'A'; or lay it in a complete circle with the apex of the tent over 'A'.

7.   Place the corner guy ropes on. Tighten them evenly. The tent will now stand alone.

8.   Put in the rest of the outside pegs and put on the guy ropes, remembering to work from both sides to keep the strain even. The pegs, ropes and seams of the tent should be in a line. The outside circle of pegs should make a perfect circle. This is known as 'starring' a bell tent.

9.   Put the brailing pegs in and place loops over the pegs.

Striking a Bell Tent

1.   Remove, scrape and stack brailing pegs, (see instructions for ridge tent).

2.   Remove all guy ropes and pegs except the four 'corners'. Slide runner up guy rope to where it is attached to tent. Tie the rope in an overhand knot.

3.   Tie the door and hook the door brailing. Have one girl hold the pole steady.

4.   Remove the four 'corner' guys and tie. Remove pegs.

5.   One girl stands at each side holding the tent out, as the girl holding the pole gently lowers it with the wind.

6.   Remove the pole. Straighten the tent to make a roughly triangular shape. Smooth out all wrinkles and sweep off dirt, etc.

7.   Fold the brailings and the ropes to the inside.

8.   Fold the tent to fit the storage space or tent bag. Make sure all the air is pressed out as you fold or roll the tent.

Pitching and Striking Other Types of Tents

There are many different kinds of tents available. Generally speaking, the first step in pitching a floored tent is to lay it out as flat and taut as possible and anchor the floor with its corner pegs.

Outside-frame tents usually have a number of poles which have to be fitted together to make the frame. Follow the directions which come with the tent.

Tents which have sectioned poles inside are usually easier to pitch if you assemble the parts outside and then insert them.

When using a tent with a floor, remember to keep it well swept.

HOW TO TAKE CARE OF YOUR TENT

Daily

(i)   As soon as the walls are dry in the morning, loop the brailings, or if they have ties, roll them and tie using a slippery hitch. (The use of a slippery hitch rather than a reef knot or bow, lets you drop the brailings very quickly in case of sudden rain.) This airs the tent and keeps it cool. Canvas becomes very hot. Even in damp weather, brailings should be looped to air the tent.

(ii)   Check the pegs and poles and make adjustments if needed to keep the tent 'set' or 'starred'. If the pole is not straight, adjust the guy ropes to straighten it.

(iii) Check the ropes occasionally every day to make sure they are tight, unless the weather is wet. (See below.)

(iv)   Don't let anything — gadgets, luggage, you — lean or rub against the canvas. You don't want to invite a leak!

(v)   Don't put pins in the canvas or use the guy ropes for a clothes line.

In wet weather

(i)   Rain shrinks the canvas and the ropes (unless made of nylon), so the guy ropes must be loosened and checked periodically during the rain. Loosen them again if they shrink and tighten more.

(ii)   If someone happens to touch the canvas and it leaks, run your finger down the course of the leak to the bottom of the tent.

(iii) Make sure no ground sheets are sticking out of the tent. They make a nice funnel for rain to run into the tent.

(iv)   In heavy rain or continued wet weather, rain may run into the tent. If so, dig a trench where it is needed so that the drips from the roof run into it. Direct the trench away from the door. The sod you remove should be carefully dug out, and replaced when trench is no longer needed.

(v)   If pegs loosen and won't stay in the wet ground, reinforce them with an extra peg hooked over the first one, or with stones, bricks, a bag of sand piled against it, or with two more pegs guyed out in a V-shape from the first.

In windy weather

(i) High winds can even carry your tent away, so keep a close eye on what's happening to it. Keep the guys tightened (if it's raining too, slacken slowly and carefully), especially on the windward side.

(ii) Keep the brailing tightly pegged down and the door closed to prevent the wind from lifting the tent.

(iii) If the brailing loop won't stay on the peg, twist the loop first to make it smaller.

(iv) If the runner slips on the guy rope, twist the rope around the runner.

(v) Follow directions for reinforcing pegs in wet ground to keep the pegs from pulling out.

(vi) Storm-lash by using long ropes from the ends of the ridge.

Storage of tents

(i) Never store a wet tent. If you strike camp in rain, and have to fold up the tents, unfold them and dry thoroughly *as soon as possible*. Wet canvas soon mildews.

(ii) Mice find folded tents a cosy place to live. If you haven't a mouseproof storage place, try putting mothballs in the tents to deter the mice

Repairing tents, pegs and poles

(i) Patches over holes can be put on with fabric adhesive. Some people prefer oval, round or house-shaped patches to square ones because the rain will run off them more readily. Stitched patches should be put on with heavy thread, preferably waxed. They should be backstitched, so that there are no spaces. Use old or pre-shrunk canvas for patches, because new material will shrink.

(ii)   In order to mend a slit make a running stitch around it. Then alternate long and short vertical stitches below and above the slit.

(iii) If a grommet has come out, replace it or use a brass curtain ring. Cover hole with a patch which has an X cut in its centre the same dimensions as the hole. Fold the flaps made by the cut over the grommet and buttonhole stitch the grommet in place. Backstitch or glue the outside of the patch. Grommets can also be made from light cord by buttonhole stitching a circle of cord.

(iv)   Badly worn, or short ropes should be replaced. Note how the other ropes are attached and do the same.

(v)   A broken runner should be replaced. Until it is, either a guyline hitch or fisherman's knot on the guy rope will let you loop it over the peg and still tighten or loosen it easily.

(vi)   Broken poles can be repaired by placing the broken ends together accurately and using shear lashing, and attaching a splint (piece of pole or wood a bit longer than the split in the pole). Tighten the lashing by inserting a wedge of wood between the pole and the splint.

(vii) Extra pegs should always be available. If they aren't, make a temporary peg from a green stick. Sharpen the end and cut a notch near the top. Or find a forked green stick and sharpen the other end. Broken guy pegs can often be cut shorter and made into brailing pegs by sharpening the end.

198

Take care of your tent pegs

(i) Always use a wooden mallet for wooden pegs.

(ii) Don't bang pegs into rock.

(iii) Don't pound in pegs with the guy rope attached. This puts a strain on the peg and the canvas. It also increases the danger of burying the rope in the ground.

(iv) Remove pegs by using another peg as a lever, or by tapping them *very* gently to loosen.

(v) Don't pull the guy rope, or brailing loop, along with the peg. This weakens the ropes.

(vi) If your mallet has a loose head, soak it in a pail of water until the wood has swollen to fit the handle again.

FURNITURE FOR YOUR CAMP HOME

That's what some camp gadgets are — furniture. Some gadgets are utensils. With wood you can easily make almost anything from a roasting stick to a dining table. You don't have to be a carpenter. You do need to know a little about wood, and a few basic hitches, knots and lashings. And you need a dash of imagination. Once you know how to make a few gadgets, you can create your own for almost any purpose.

You will need wood. You can use dead wood that isn't too brittle. If you can break it easily with your hands, you know it won't last long as a piece of furniture. Green wood is ideal. Sometimes you will see utilities workers cutting down unwanted trees and they are usually happy to give branches away. Sometimes people are clearing out undergrowth in woods and will give you what you need. Old hockey sticks and curling brooms are

CAMP GADGETS

TRY THESE GADGETS . . . INVENT SOME MORE YOURSELF!

Look up the Inbetween on Lashing to learn how to do the lashings you need for your gadgets.

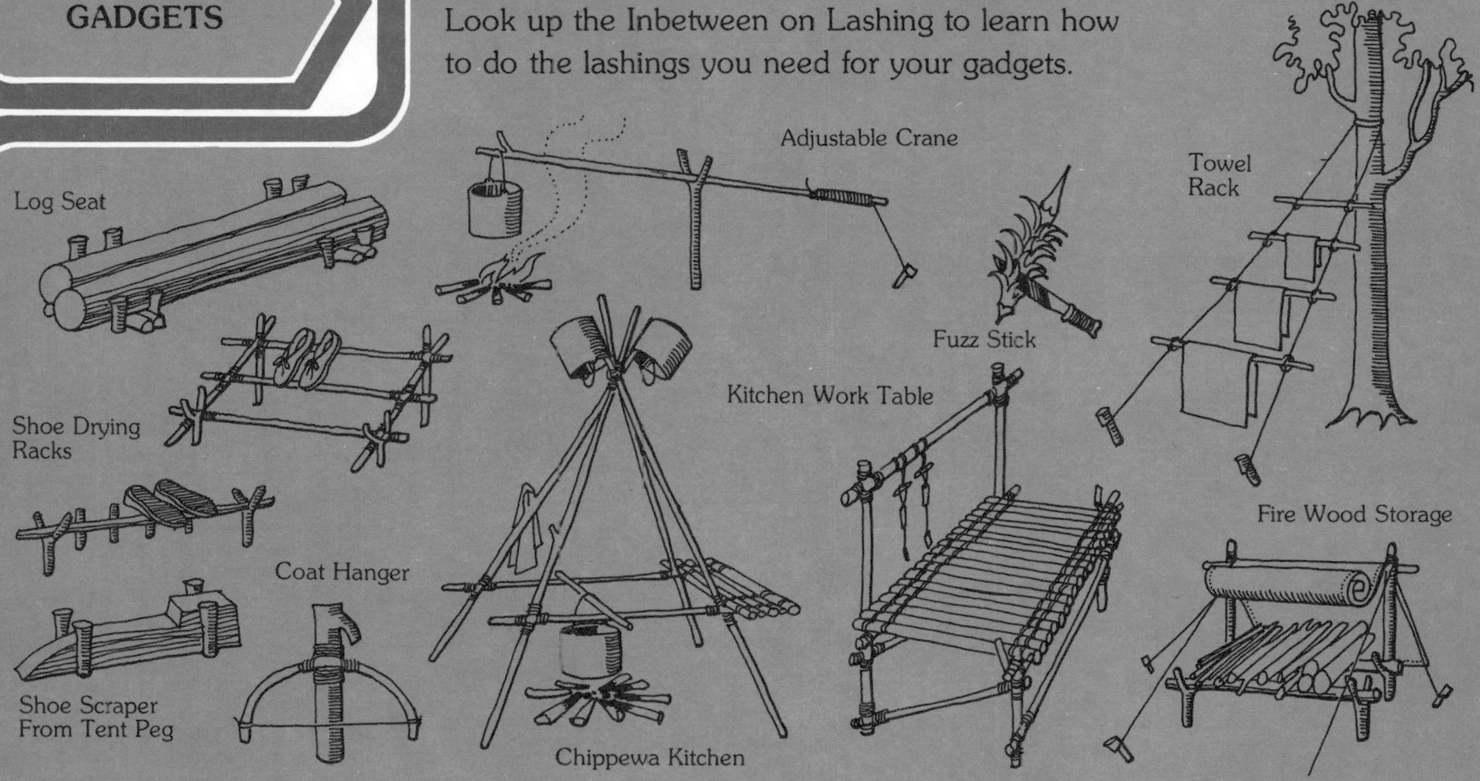

Towel Rack

Fire Wood Storage

Fuzz Stick

Adjustable Crane

Kitchen Work Table

Chippewa Kitchen

Log Seat

Shoe Drying Racks

Coat Hanger

Shoe Scraper From Tent Peg

thrown out by hockey and curling teams. They make great gadget wood. If you have no other source of wood, buy dowelling. *Never cut living trees.*

(i) If the gadget is to go into the ground, sharpen the ends with a hatchet. Make a hole in the ground with a tent peg and mallet.

(ii) If you have a saw (or pruning shears for thin pieces of wood), use them to make the ends tidy.

(iii) Look for forked sticks. They have many uses.

(iv) Lashing cord should be strong. If you can break it by pulling on both ends, you know it will not give you good service.

(v) Lashing cord can be reused many times, *if* you take apart your gadget carefully when you are finished with it. Don't cut the cord; untie it. (One reason for using proper hitches and knots is that they will untie easily.) Wind cord around your fingers and tie into neat little bundles, or wind it around a stick. Small pieces of cord (within reason) can be joined together with a reef knot. When joining cord of different thicknesses, a sheet bend may be used.

Try these gadgets . . . invent some more yourself!

Look up the Inbetween on Lashing to learn how to do the lashings you need for your gadgets.

KNOTS AND HITCHES

If you know how to tie the right knot or hitch for the right purpose, you will find it very useful. Your parcels will stay securely tied, but the receiver will be able to get into them easily — and be able to reuse your cord. Your boat won't drift away, nor will your dog or donkey. Your clothes line will stay put and your flag will remain flying.

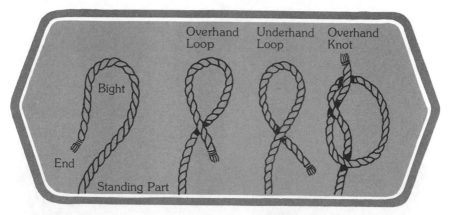

Learn these five simple basic steps and the rest is easy:

1. A rope has a working end (it does most of the work as you tie) and a standing part (which stands about, but which is usually the part you pull to tighten the knot).

2. The bight — it's not a loop, just the working end bent back against the standing end. (illustrated)

3. An overhand loop — the working end crosses over the standing part.

4. An underhand loop — the working end passes under the standing part.

5. An overhand knot — the working end is passed through a loop and can be tightened.

Once you have these basics straight, you're ready to try some knots. Follow the diagrams and practise. When you think you can do a knot without looking at the diagram, try it and check with the picture. Then try it five times; then twice with your eyes shut and twice behind your back. You've got it? Try a week later and if you haven't forgotten, the knot is probably yours for life. It's fun to have knot-tying contests with some friends to see who's the fastest knotter. Remember, if you don't know what it's used for, there's not much point in learning it!

Knots to join two ropes together

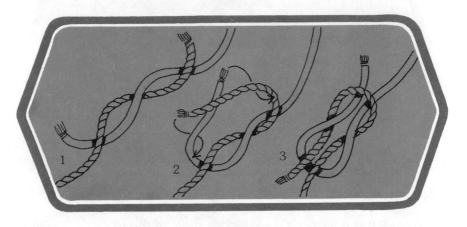

Reef (or Square) Knot This makes a flat knot and is used when both ropes are the same thickness. Don't use it when the ropes are of different thicknesses because it may slip.

Lay the two ends together, with the left end over the right end. Twist the left end behind and around in front of the right end. Then put the same end (which is now on the *right* side) over the other end, twist behind the bight and up through again. Tighten by pulling standing parts. Think — left over right and under; right over left and under.

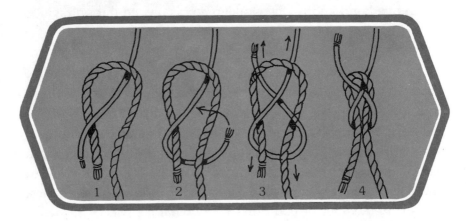

Sheet Bend (Bend means tie, and sheet is what ropes are called on boats.)

Although this is a rather bumpy knot, it will never come undone by itself. Strain on it simply tightens it more.

Make a bight in the end of rope (the heavier if different thicknesses). Bring the end of the other rope up through the bight, around the standing part and back under itself, coming out over the bight. Tighten by pulling the two standing parts.

Hitches for tying ropes to objects

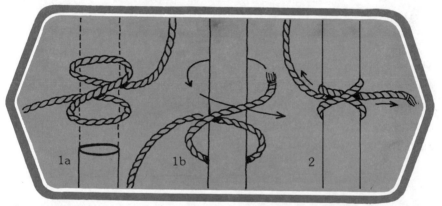

Clove Hitch If you can drop the hitch, which is composed of two loops, over the object (like a short post or the toggle on a flag), you can use method A. If you can't because the object is too high (like a tree), use method B. Remember—the working end does all the work.

This hitch should not be used if the object being tied can move, so don't tie up a boat or animal with it.

A Make two overhand loops. Put the second one behind the first and drop over the post.

B Take a turn around the post, with working end cross over the standing part and make a second turn. Bring working end up through, under loop so formed.

Other useful hitches

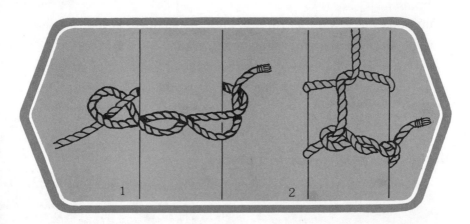

Timber Hitch You can use this to drag heavy objects using a rope. Put the working end around the object, then over the standing part (and under), twisting several times on the loop. Add a simple hitch at the other end of the object if you're pulling something.

Guy Line Hitch If a guy line runner is broken, or if you have made a gadget (for example, a flagpole) which needs guy lines, use this hitch. It is a clove hitch on its own standing part with an extra hitch.

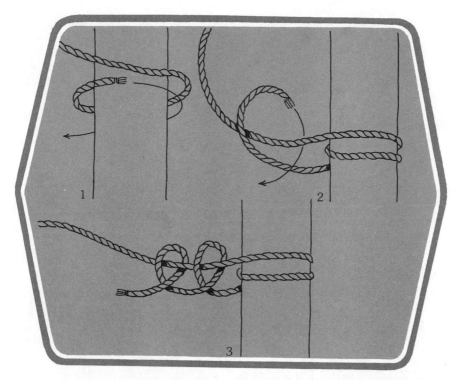

Round Turn and Two Half Hitches This hitch is made by taking a turn around the object you're tying the rope to and then making two half hitches on the standing part. This is useful for tying a moving object to a post. If you know how to do the blanket stitch in embroidery, you will realize that it is just a series of half hitches. Sew the half hitches very close together and you've got the buttonhole stitch!

Slippery Hitch This is useful when you have rolled tent brailings and want to secure them but also be able to let them down in a hurry.

To tie, cross working end of one rope over the standing part (the other rope) and instead of tying a complete overhand knot, just slip a bight near the top partly through. To untie, just pull the free end, like undoing a bow in a shoelace.

206

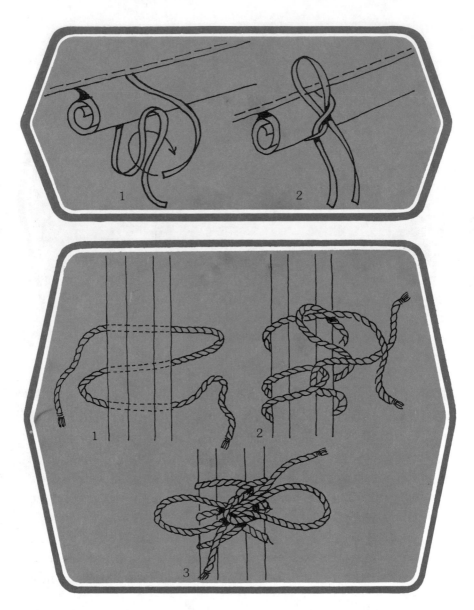

Pole Hitch This ties bundles of poles together securely, especially if you put one on each end of the bundle. Make an 'S' in the middle of your rope. Lay the poles on top. Put the ends through the loops on the opposite side. Pull tightly and tie in a bow.

Other Knots

Bowline This has been called the 'Queen of Knots'. It makes a loop which won't slip or jam, and is thus a good rescue knot. Make an overhand loop on the standing part (like writing the figure 6). Bring the working end *up* through this loop, then around the back of the standing part. Put it down into the loop. Tighten by pulling the standing part as you hold on to the end and loop. Make sure you have the loop the size you need.

Packer's Knot (or Figure-of-Eight) This makes a loop which *will* slip, and is therefore very useful for tying up parcels and bedrolls. The loop is made by passing the working end around the standing part and then in a figure-of-eight fashion around itself. The loop will slide up and down the standing part to loosen or tighten.

Tie a parcel and a bedroll the same way. Put your packer's knot loop over the parcel or bedroll. Tighten as much as possible. Bring working end around the other end of parcel making a half hitch when you come to the loop. End where you began with two half hitches. This will not come undone. For your bedroll, you need not ever untie your packer's knot. Just loosen when necessary.

208

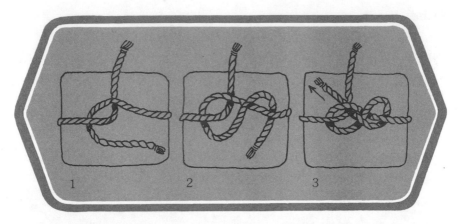

Figure-of-Eight Knot as a Stopper Knot Sheets on a sailboat need a stopper knot at their ends to keep them from going through the rings. Make handles on a box the same way. Use a stopper knot at the end of the sheet or rope. Make a tight figure-of-eight on itself.

Rope too long? Shorten it with a Sheep Shank or a Chain Knot.

You may want to temporarily shorten a rope. Use a sheep shank.

Sheep Shank Make an 'S' to take up the slack. Make an under-hand loop at 'A' and slide it over the 'A' bight and pull tight. Make an underhand loop at 'B'. Slide it over the 'B' bight, and pull tight. This will need a stick put through each loop if it has to serve more than temporarily.

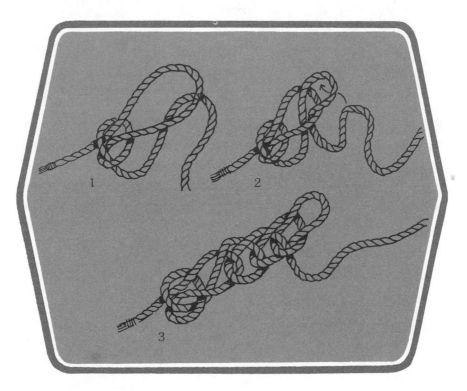

Chain Knot This is how you begin to crochet. It is known as SC for Single Crochet. It is useful for entertaining young children. You can teach them to do it easily with a small ball of wool and they will think they are knitting! And it is a good way to shorten a rope.

Make an overhand loop. Lay it over the standing part and pull a loop through. Lay this loop over the standing part and pull a loop through. Continue until the rope is as short as you wish, then slip the end through the final loop.

Fisherman's Knot This is used to tie two fine lines, like fishing lines together. It is made by tying an overhand knot at the end of each line and running the end of the opposite line through the loops. Tighten the loops separately. Then pull both standing parts to bring the overhand knots together. This makes wet lines easy to untie. If using a single rope, pull the overhand knots away from each other, and you can make a handle for a pot or can.

LASHINGS

When two or more poles or sticks are tied together with cord or rope, we say they are lashed together. There are different kinds of lashings, depending on how you want the poles tied to each other.

Square Lashing ties poles at right angles

Make a clove hitch on the upright. Bring the working end down on top of pole 'A' vertically, horizontally behind pole 'B', vertically up the other side of 'A', horizontally behind pole 'B'. Continue

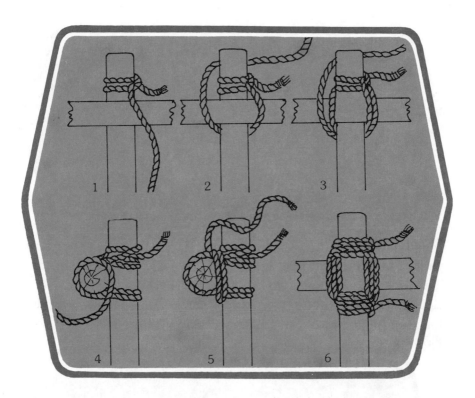

doing this several times, making sure you are making a square each time with your cord, and keeping it tidy and tight. Then what really tightens lashings is the frapping. This is done by winding the cord tightly between the poles. End with a clove hitch on the cross-piece and tuck in the end.

Another way to square lash is to place the middle point of your cord around the upright. Then bring both ends down around the crosspiece. Go around the back of the upright below the cross-piece. Bring both ends up over the crosspiece again, around and upright and continue in this manner. Frap and tie with a reef knot. This method is not as tidy-looking as the previous method since the ends are crossed each time at the back. It should hold just as well.

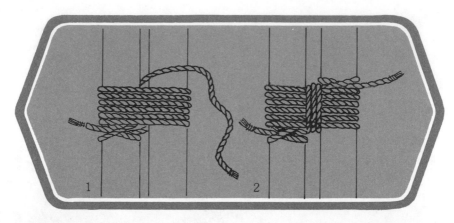

Shear Lashing is used to tie two (or more) poles together in a parallel fashion. You may want one long pole, for example, but have only short ones. Two or three can be shear lashed. Tie a clove hitch around one, then bind the two poles together tightly. Frap, and end with a clove hitch, tucking in the end.

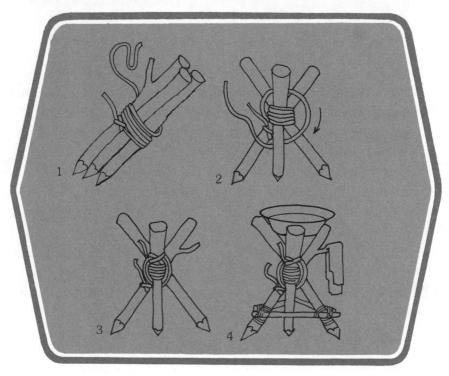

Tripod Lashing is used to tie three poles together to make a tripod, as in a washstand. Lay the three poles together. Start with a clove hitch on one. Bind the three together. Spread the poles so that they will stand. Frap tightly in all the spaces and end with a clove hitch on one pole, tucking in the end.

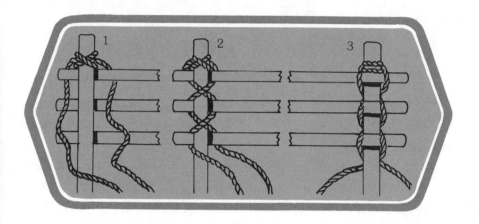

Continuous Lashing — If you want to make a table top or join sticks together to make a broad, flat surface for some other purpose, use continuous lashing. Your sticks should be all the same size to make a flat and tidy table top.

Double a long piece of lashing cord — about three times the length of your finished table top. Place the double end around a stick that will support the top sticks and be perpendicular to them. Cross the cord, bring it under the first horizontal stick, then up on top and cross it again. Repeat until all the sticks have been lashed onto the support stick. End with a clove hitch. Do the same with another support stick at the other side of the top sticks.

Whipping — Some kinds of rope fray very easily, making the ends hard to tie and eventually shortening the rope. The ends of nylon and polypropylene rope are usually melted in a match flame to seal the ends and prevent fraying.

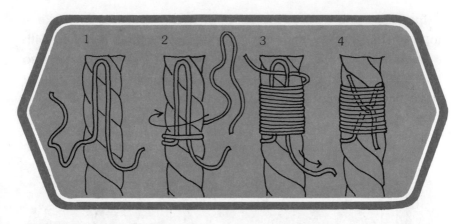

Rope made from natural materials such as cotton hemp and sisal, should be whipped. You will need a piece of twine about 15 cm. long. Make a bight in one end. Lay it alongside the end of the rope you are whipping. About 5 mm. from the end, start wrapping the twine *tightly and evenly* for about 2 cm. (depending on the thickness of the rope you are whipping). Pull the end through the loop, then pull the other end of the twine so that the loop is pulled about halfway down under the wrapping. Trim. If you have made the whipping tight, you will not be able to push it off the end of the rope.

"It ain't no use to grumble and complain;
It's jest as cheap and easy to rejoice;
When God sorts out the weather and sends rain —
Why, rain's my choice."

James Whitcombe Riley

IS RAIN YOUR CHOICE?

Rain or shine, life in camp goes on as usual. It's special to be able to do things in the rain for which you might think you need good weather — like cooking over an open fire, or hiking, or almost anything but sunbathing! If it's raining cats and dogs, you won't want to be out in it except when absolutely necessary. A nice, gentle, warm rain, however, won't stop you from doing all sorts of things. You should be dressed for the rain, of course — rubber boots, raincoat and hat.

Try these activities on a rainy day in camp.

(i)   Make up a rainy day yell or a rainy day song.

(ii)   Measure the rainfall.

(iii)   Challenge other patrols to a Rainy TV Show — make up skits based on popular TV shows, the only requirement being that the skit is set in the rain (even if you actually perform it in an indoor shelter).

(iv)   Make up a Haiku poem about rain. Haiku is a form of Japanese poetry. It has three lines and does not rhyme. The first line must contain five syllables (could be five words or one word), the second line must be composed of seven syllables, and the third line has five syllables. What kind of word picture can you create? Here's a sample of Haiku.

> *The rain hits my head,*
> *Runs silently off my chin,*
> *Then pings on my boot.*

(v)   Have a fire lighting contest to see who can boil water first, or burn through a piece of string tied tightly across a line where the fires are to be laid. Place the string 40 or 50 cm. above the ground.

(vi) Find out about soil erosion in the rain by going on an erosion find. Look for places where rain is washing soil away. Find out where it goes, and what keeps soil in other places from being washed away.

(vii) Look for birds, insects, mammals and amphibians. What do they do in the rain? Worms might be escaping from Guides looking for them for fish bait!

(viii) Have a riddle and joke contest. (Some people are sad in the rain; don't encourage them — provide laughter.) You might even end up with a camp joke book.

(ix) Add your own favourite camp rainy day activities here.

GAMES AT CAMP — WIDE AND ADVENTUROUS

Wide games have always been part of the fun at Scout and Guide camps. If you liked playing hide-and-seek when you were smaller, you will love the adventure of a good wide game.

Wide games probably originated in both hide-and-seek type games and in military exercises. B-P knew how men sharpened their wits and powers of observation when they took part in exercises. They had to act as if the danger were real, and react as if their lives and the lives of those whom they were protecting depended on it. He made up such situations for Scouts, and called them wide games — games meant to be played over a wide area and a fair length of time.

Wide games often depend on the use of stalking skills. Stalking

STALKING ANIMALS

means to sneak up on something or somebody without being seen, heard or smelled. Photographers stalk wild life to take pictures. Naturalists stalk wild life to observe how birds and animals live. Detectives stalk criminals to capture them. Hunters stalk wild life — often unnecessarily because they don't need the food — to kill.

A good stalker can move silently. She can freeze immediately because movement gives the stalker away. She knows that wearing clothing that blends with the background (called camouflage) helps. She knows that if the wind is behind her it will carry her scent to what she is stalking, so she stalks from a position facing the wind. She knows how to look for good cover — trees, shrubs, grasses, rocks, buildings — to hide her as much as possible.

Try these games

Camouflage This is best played in a place where there is good cover. The leader stands in an open, conspicuous, central spot with her eyes closed (blindfolded if necessary) for five minutes. During this time the players all hide, but they must be able to see the leader from their hiding place. A signal is given (like a blast on a whistle) and the leader opens her eyes. Within a pre-arranged time limit and without moving from her place although she may turn around, she must see how many hiders she can spot.

This is excellent practice in keeping still. What usually gives the hiders away (other than something like a red jacket!) is their movement. It's amazing how itchy your leg gets when you're trying to keep perfectly still, and leaning over to scratch can give you away.

Fireflies Night games are especially exciting. You've probably seen real fireflies that look as if they are switching headlights off and on. To play the game you need two teams. Every member of A Team has a flashlight, and is a firefly. Team B tries to capture the fireflies.

Team A is given several minutes to hide within whatever boundaries are set for the game. Then the leader blows a whistle. The Fireflies must switch on their flashlights for a few seconds. The fireflies should keep changing position. Team B tries to capture Team A. A good means of capture is to have a strip of fabric or coloured plastic (stuck in Team A's belts) which must be taken. If such physical means of capture is too difficult, call out the name of a spotted Team A member.

The leader should blow the 'flashlights on' signal at regular intervals. At the end of ten or fifteen minutes, sides can be changed. The team with the most captives wins.

Secret Assignments One patrol is chosen to be the Guards. The other patrols are given sealed envelopes containing assignments. It is best to draw straws for these since no patrol really wants the

Guard position. Set boundaries for the game and a time limit with a signal (like three long blasts of a whistle) to denote the end of the game, if every patrol hasn't returned.

Give each team its envelope. Tell them to go to a starting point about five minutes' walk away before they can open their envelopes and begin. Warn them to plan and organize how they are going to carry out their assignment. Anyone seen by a Guard is considered captured if she is seen and her name called. The Guards are given boundaries beyond which they may not go.

The kind of assignment you make up depends on where you are playing the game. The guarded territory might be your tent areas or it might be in some other place. The following sample assignments assume that the guarded area is where the patrol tents and kitchens are. The assignments should *not* involve taking or harming personal or camp equipment, nor putting something up the flagpole.

Some Ideas for Assignments:

(a) Using a natural object, write the name of your patrol on another natural object and place it in a pail you will find hanging on a tree branch near a tent.

(b) Using natural materials make a rope at least two metres long. Tie it to the leg of the table nearest the stores tent.

(c) Using natural materials make a container, and fill it with water. Place it on the table closest to the Kingfisher tent.

(d) Using the pencil enclosed and something natural to write on, get close enough to three of the Guards to hear and write down at least five sentences of their conversation. Then place this under the guy ropes of the stores tent.

When a patrol (or any member of it) has completed the assignment successfully, she should shout her patrol name and the word 'successful'. Captured patrol members must sit (quietly) in a preassigned spot, and successful patrols join them.

Secret Formula One patrol is a group of scientists who have discovered a way to make bicycle gears which will never break. They have written their formula on a piece of paper. The other patrols are the employees and owners of a company which makes bicycle gears. This formula will soon put them out of business. They want to capture the scientists and their formula. The scientists want to reach the police who will protect them and their formula.

Set boundaries, a time limit and a means of capture (cloth strips, contact or recognition by name). Write out an imaginary formula (make it look as authentic as possible) and cut into as many pieces as there are scientists. Give each scientist one piece and station her a good distance away from the police (the leaders). The other patrols must try to capture them before they reach the police safely with their pieces of the formula. There should be a reasonable 'safe' area near the police where the other patrols cannot go.

MAKE UP YOUR OWN WIDE GAMES!

CAMPFIRE

Campfire Songs

"Come, come, light up the fire, come, come
join in the ring; Here find dreams to inspire,
stories to tell, music to sing."

Those are the words of the 'Sussex Campfire Opening' (you'll find the music in *Jubilee Song Book*), known and loved by Guides all over the world. A campfire which leaves you with dreams to inspire doesn't just happen by accident. It has a shape or a form, something like this:

		More serious		
	Light-hearted		Ends quietly	
Starts quietly				
Opening chosen from a variety of campfire openings. A suitable verse.	Fun things like action songs, yells, campfire games, funny skits.	Songs that are quieter or a serious skit or story.	Quiet songs Vesper Prayer.	Taps

A good campfire programme always has a leader. It could be you! Whoever it is, she should:

— have the campfire programme written down. (If she wants to include other people's favourite items, she asks ahead of time and puts them in the programme. It breaks the atmosphere to ask during campfire if anyone has a song they'd like.)

— announce the songs and other items clearly.

— lead each song (or ask someone else ahead of time) by giving the opening note strongly before beginning.

—know what's coming next on the programme so that she can announce it without long pauses.

— avoid the distraction of using books or song sheets at campfire.

Does your company have a notebook listing the songs, games, yells, readings and prayers that you know? Such a list is called a repertoire. Having your repertoire listed means that you can find what you know easily and lets you have lots of variety, if you have it at hand when planning. Most of the songs Guides sing are found in the song books listed in the bibliography at the back of this book. It's a good idea to put the song book's initials beside the song title in your list. Leave lots of room between the different sections of your list so that you can add new songs you learn. If the song comes from another country you might want to put that fact on your list too.

Having a campfire on a special theme is fun. Try an International campfire, or one made up of outdoor songs.

Some songs are more suitable to sing to pass the time when washing dishes or hiking. Save those long, loud songs (like 'The ants came marching') for such occasions. They don't add much to a nice campfire atmosphere.

Learning new songs

If you have the words *and* the music, it's easy to learn a new song. If you have a musical instrument, you can practise the songs. If you don't, find someone who does. Musical people always enjoy learning new songs and helping others. Your Guider knows where you can buy tapes (cassette and reel) which have many, many Guide songs on them. The tapes were made to help you learn to sing the songs, including rounds, alto parts and descants.

If all the Guides all across Canada knew many of the same songs, think what a glorious campfire we could have if we all got together! If you learn the music and words from the same books, this can happen. Imagine what it would be like if all the Guides around the world got together! . . . the planet earth would probably go right out into space on all those sound waves!

Campfire Yells

Campfire yells have been part of Guiding and Scouting since B-P wrote *Scouting for Boys*. Somebody once wrote that it was because the word boys rhymes with noise, which can't be the real reason because girls love yells at campfire too.

A campfire yell is short, usually built up around a few words or sounds, often with actions, and often built up in several parts. One yell is enough for a campfire programme— more than enough, perhaps — so don't overwork them. Here are some examples for you to try.

Een-Gon-Yama Chorus

This is part yell, part song. B-P heard the Zulu soldiers sing it during the African wars. It was sung in honour of a great hunter or chief. The words mean: "He is a lion, he is a lion. No, he is greater than a lion: he is a hippopotamus." It should be sung exactly in time and with great precision and dignity. Many different actions have been invented to go with it. Sometimes it starts very quietly and builds up to a very loud climax with the second line. Sometimes one half sings the first part, the other half the second part. Experiment with different actions, remembering what the words mean and how the Zulus used it.

SOLO (Leader). Chorus.

Een - gon-yâm-a   Gon-yâm-a,   In-voo-boo!

Ya - Boh!   Ya - Boh!   In - voo - boo.

Rockets

Divide the group into two parts to imitate a rocket going up.

1st part — place palm of hand in front of mouth and keep it moving in a circular motion while hissing

2nd part — place palm in front of mouth, moving it in a circular motion while whistling down the scale

Start quietly, building up more loudly until the leader is satisfied. The leader gives a signal (like hands together over head), and everyone shouts deeply and *very* loudly, "Boom!"

City Yell

Here's a yell for Guides in a big city. Where it says 'my city' use the name of your city. Divide the group into four parts.

ALL — "my city, city, city" (said in a stage whisper)

1st part — (rest continue with "my city" until their part) — "High rise apartments" repeated while raising arms into a tower shape and looking upwards

2nd part — "heavy traffic beep-beep" (said in a deep voice)

3rd part — "busy stores, jingle, jingle" (high voice while fingers make cash register actions)

4th part — "people rushing, bustle, bustle" (lots of 's' sound and stamp feet or slap knees)

When all have joined in with their parts, indicate with your hands an increase in volume until it's really loud. Bring your hands together and on this signal, everyone shouts "my city".

Canada Yell

All make a circle, kneeling, facing on an angle in one direction.
(Actions)

1. 4 Canoe paddling beats — (while saying soflty)
"swish, swish, swish,
swish"

2. hand to ear — 4 loon cries

3. touch shoulder ahead — beaver chewing sound,
point tail slap

4. 2 canoe beats — "swish, swish"

5. 4 FAST canoe beats — "swish, swish, swish,
swish"

6. canoe swamps — "glub, glub, glub,
glub"

NOW CREATE SOME YELLS OF YOUR OWN!

GUIDES' OWN IS

A time when Guides come together to express their feelings about the things that matter most in life: their relationships with other people, their relationship with God, the way they would like the world to be, the troubles they have, the joys they have.

Made up of many things Music played on an instrument can set many different moods. Songs and hymns have words which often say just what you're feeling. Prayers which you make up or find in a book tell God of your thankfulness, your love of Him, the things you're sorry for, the things you hope for. Drama can express deep feelings. Act out a story or a parable, using dialogue, or using mime as a narrator reads. Some songs can be acted out too, and creative dance, well done, can be a very lovely expression of how you feel. Poetry and short readings can be used.

Loveliest when you try to make the place you hold it lovelier. In the outdoors, find the place where everyone can sit comfortably and where God's beauties of nature surround you. If you want, make a focal point with flowers, and a cross if you are Christians, or some other symbol of your religion. Indoors, you can use pictures, slides, and other visual aids to help the words you hear mean more.

Best when it is planned by several people. Find out from other Guides what they would like to happen in the Guides' Own. Have as many Guides take an active part as you can. If someone has to say or read something, give them practice time and encourage them to speak slowly and clearly. Sometimes it's hard to read in front of people and you may want to have two or three people read together so that they will feel more confident.

Often held at camp when Guides have been living and working together; or around Thinking Day; or at the time of company or religious celebrations; or whenever you want to express your thankfulness and love together.

CAMP HATS — CRESTS — CAMPFIRE PONCHOS

Camp hats were really designed to keep the sun out of your eyes, and help prevent sunstroke, and don't be surprised if that's what adults tell you. Every Guide knows that their greatest use is as a place to sew crests, swaps and all kinds of interesting little things you can make. A really creatively decorated camp hat can tell the story of your camping career — where you've been, what you did, whom you met.

Guides have set fashion trends in camp hat wearing by

turning the brim down all the way round
turning the brim down only at the back
turning the brim up all the way round
turning the brim up at one side
wearing it away down over their eyes
wearing it . . . well, you decide the way that best suits your personality!

If you are going to a special camp, or going to wear camp uniform where members of the general public will see you, you may be asked to wear an undecorated camp hat. (Even the proud owners of camp hats where the blue fabric is scarcely visible, will admit that they feel better in public in a *plain* hat — one gets tired of people trying to read one's head.) It's a good idea to have a plain camp hat for such times.

MAKE YOUR OWN PONCHO AND SIT ROUND THE CAMPFIRE IN COMFORT

Those chilly nights when the sun has gone down can be shiver free if you have a warm poncho. You can put your sense of design to work as you arrange the crests you've collected, your old Brownie badges and perhaps even do some embroidery. These directions show you two easy ways to make a poncho.

You can use almost any kind of warm fabric. Melton cloth is very cosy. If you have an old blanket, use it.

You can even make a lightweight patchwork poncho with the legs from blue jeans after making cut-offs. (Line it for warmth.) Now look up the Thrift Badge requirements.

228

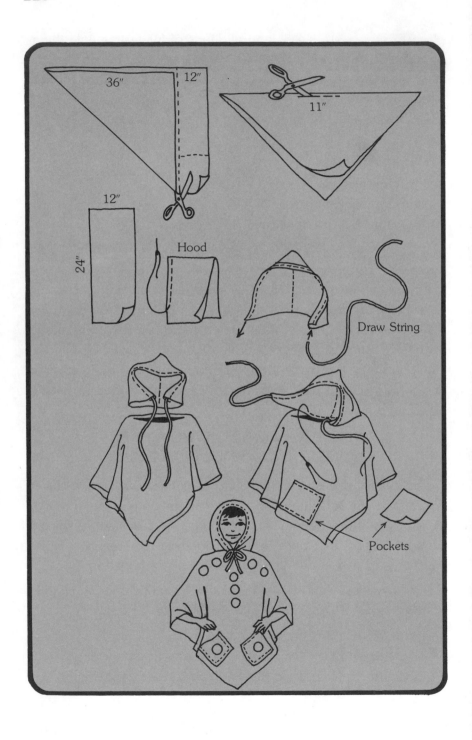

PONCHO INSTRUCTIONS

Make a poncho from an old blanket or from new fabric.

1. For the main body of the poncho you need a square. If you are using an old blanket this will mean cutting off a strip at one end.

2. Cut a neck opening slit, being careful not to cut too large an opening.

3. From the strip which you cut from the blanket in forming your poncho square, or from a new piece of fabric, cut a piece of cloth large enough for a hood. Fold it in half. The fold forms the top of the hood. Seam one side to form the back of the hood.

4. Sew a casing around the front edge of the hood, through which a drawstring can be run. Use a skate lace, a piece of cord or something else suitable for the drawstring.

5. Now sew the bottom edge of the hood to the neck opening of the poncho.

6. Finish the raw edges of the poncho, however you wish: blanket stitch in wool, hem or sew on a fringe. If you wish make a pocket from any excess material. And sew on your badges and crests!

THE FLAG OF CANADA

Canada's flag was adopted by Parliament and proclaimed by the Queen on February 15, 1965. It is a red flag, twice as long as it is wide, with a white square the width of the flag in its centre. The white square contains a single red maple leaf with eleven points. There is no significance in the number of points; they merely make a pleasing design. Red and white have been Canada's official colours since 1921.

The Canadian Flag is a symbol of Canada and deserves our respect and care. It should not touch the ground nor drag in the water. When a flag is badly torn or faded, it should be burned.

Flags which are made to be carried on poles may be dedicated and this is usually done in church. Dedicated flags are commonly called 'colours' and should never be left uncased, unless guarded or kept in a place of worship on display.

The proper way to hold a flag for carrying is to gather up the fly (the side of the flag which flies freely) in your right hand and hold it along with the pole at face height. Your knuckles should face *outward*. Your elbow should be close to your side. It is not customary for Guides to wear gloves when carrying flags unless the weather is cold.

Marching with the Flag

1. The Canadian Flag is carried on the marching right. If several flags are being carried, it is in the centre.

2. A colour party is customarily composed of three people: one bearer, who carries the flag, and two escorts or guards. Since the bearer has the flag in front of her face, she depends on her escorts to guide her.

3. It is not necessary, and really not proper, to use escorts in a place of worship which is traditionally considered 'sanctuary', i.e. a safe place.

4. On ceremonial occasions when Guides are in horseshoe formation, the colours (both the Canadian Flag and the World Flag which is the company colour) may be marched on in an impressive way. The two colour parties are apart from the horseshoe, usually beyond its foot, or off to one side. Each bearer receives her flag from someone in charge and the two colour parties get into position. The Canadian Flag party marches up the left side (from the viewpoint of the captain) of the horseshoe and the World Flag party up the right side. They halt at the mouth of the horseshoe, after wheeling into position be-

tween the Captain or person in charge and the mouth of the horse-shoe. The Canadian Flag is closest to the Captain. Both colour parties are facing each other and have sufficient room to march to the opposite side. On the command, "March on the colours", they cross in front of the Captain. On reaching the opposite sides, they halt, about turn, and stand facing inwards. The Canadian Flag is now in the place of honour, on the Captain's right, and the World Flag on her left. The bearer may rest the pole vertically on the floor at her right side and stand at ease if given the order, "Stand at ease".

To "March off" the colours, the order "March off the colours" is given, and the colour parties cross in front of the Captain and return to the place where they received the flags.

Where space is limited, the colour parties may be marched on separately. If there is not enough space for three to march abreast, the order "into file, right (or left) turn" may be given. The right-hand guard moves ahead of the bearer, and the left-hand guard behind her.

5. It takes practice to perform flag ceremonials well. Members of the colour parties should be in full and proper uniform and should be able to march

correctly and have good posture. It is a privilege to be in a colour party.

Displaying the Flag

1. If the flag is displayed flat against a wall in a building with another flag, the staffs are crossed. The Canadian Flag is on the left as you face it. Its staff is in front of the other flag's staff.

2. In a place of worship, the flag should stand upright on its staff in a suitable holder, or hang at right angles from the wall. If it is in the chancel or on a platform, it is on the congregation's left. If it is in the nave or where the congregation sits, it is on the right.

3. The flag should never be draped, nor used to cover a table. On a speaker's platform, it should be either on the wall above and behind the speaker, or on a staff on the speaker's right.

Flying the Flag from a Staff

1. The flag is raised after sunrise and lowered before sunset.

2. A flag is flown at half-mast as a sign of mourning for someone who has died. To do this, raise the flag to the top of the pole (the masthead), then bring it slowly down to half-staff. It is said this space symbolizes the space

that would be occupied by the standard (the personal flag) of the person who has died. To lower a flag flown at half-mast, raise it to the top first, then lower it.

3. If you are in distress and need help, fly the flag upside down. It is an internationally known sign of distress.

4. If flags of more than one country (or the World Flag or provincial flags) are being flown, separate staffs of the same height should be used. When two flags are being flown, the Canadian Flag should be on the left as you face the flags. When three flags are flown, the Canadian Flag should be central. When more than three are being flown, the Canadian Flag may be the left, or one may be flown at each end.

5. If you must fly two flags from one staff, the Canadian Flag should be at the top.

6. When raising more than one flag, they should be hoisted and lowered at the same time. If this is impossible, the Canadian Flag should be raised first, and lowered last.

Folding the Flag for Hoisting

1. Holding the flag flat, one person with the hoist (the side that goes up the pole) and one with the fly, fold it in

half, taking the bottom to the top.

2. Fold the fly to meet the edge of the red stripe nearest the hoist.

3. Fold the flag again to meet the same red stripe.

4. Fold the hoist's red stripe over the folded flag. Tuck the strop into the fold. Leave the toggle on top of the folded flag.

Hoisting the Flag

This is often done when Guides are in horseshoe formation. There is a colour party of three. They may have the flag folded in a safe place or held by someone near the horseshoe and they may fall out (usually on order from the Captain) from their places in the horseshoe. If they are not in the horseshoe, they may wait at one side with the flag until the horseshoe is formed. It is also effective to have the colour party in the centre at the foot of the horseshoe. In this case, the girls on either side of the colour party should move to close the gap when the colour party leaves, opening it again on their return.

1. The flag bearer carries the folded flag flat on her open palms, holding the edges securely with her thumbs. Nylon flags are slippery and unfold very readily. The escort on her right

attaches the strop of the flag to one end of the halyard, using a *sheet bend*. The escort on her left attaches the other end of the halyard to the toggle, using a *clove hitch*, unless the halyard has a permanent loop. Make sure the toggle is pulled all the way through the loops formed by the clove hitch.

2. The escort on the *right* of the bearer raises the flag briskly to the top of the pole. The bearer can help guide if necessary. If the National Anthem is sung, she holds the flag at the top before securing the halyard to the pole using a clove hitch, or round turn and two half hitches. (The latter should be used if there is any danger of the halyard being loosened.)

3. The colour party does not join in the singing of the National Anthem, but remains at attention.

Lowering the Flag

The colour party members return to their places. When the flag is to be lowered, they reassemble at the flagpole. A whistle is often blown to signify that the flag is going to be brought down and everyone within sight stands at attention. After lowering, another whistle is blown. Then the flag is untied, folded and put away.

Commands for the Colour Party

If the colour party is in the horseshoe, the Captain or person in charge usually gives the command, "fall out". The colour party takes a step forward, and two back. The bearer goes to where the flag is, says "Colour party, fall in" and her escorts fall in beside her.

Bearer: "Colour party, forward march."

If they can march straight to the flagpole, no further command is given until they reach it.

Bearer: "Colour party, halt."

They proceed to raise the flag as above. If the pole is not straight ahead of the starting position, the bearer will have to give the appropriate command to right or left turn or wheel — whatever suits the occasion.

After the flag has been raised and the halyard secured to the pole, the bearer gives the orders to leave.

Bearer: "Colour party, about turn." (Or right or left turn, depending on the position.) "Forward march."

When they reach the place from which they began, the bearer gives the command "Halt". Then she steps forward, turns and faces her escorts, and continues "Colour party, fall out." They return to their places.

You may be able to think of some other ways to carry out this ceremony. Just remember to treat the flag with respect and to do the ceremony with dignity. Make sure the escorts know how to tie the clove hitch and sheet bend properly and quickly. Nothing takes away dignity faster than having to wait while knot-tiers fumble. If you are nervous or unsure, practise ahead of time. Ask someone who knows how to tie the knots to stand near the flagpole the first time you do it, so that you can get help quickly and quietly.

WHEN THE FLAG IS BEING RAISED OR LOWERED, OR PASSES BY ON PARADE, STAND AT ATTENTION. IT'S YOUR COUNTRY'S FLAG. BE PROUD OF IT.

If you are visiting in another country, or with a group which carries out their ceremony differently, it is courteous to do as they do. Although we do not salute the flag in Guide flag ceremonies, if you are with a group which does, you may salute by holding your hand as for the Guide Sign — three fingers raised and thumb over the little finger — and bringing it up to the side of your hat.

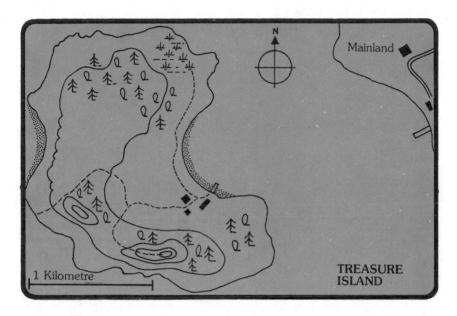

This is a map of the island explored by the Guides in the story. Can you guess what the symbols on the map mean?

TOPOGRAPHIC MAPS

On the next page you'll find more map symbols. They are used on topographic maps in most parts of the world. You don't have to memorize them since most topographic maps have a key to the symbols used on them, either along the margin or on the back of the map. It's fun to figure them out.

A topographic map is just a drawing of a place as if you were seeing it from the air. The scale is usually 1:50,000. This means that one unit (centimetre, inch, etc.) is the same as 50,000 units on the ground. That is large enough to allow lots of detail to be put on the map.

TOPOGRAPHICAL SYMBOLS

Village		Telephone	
School		Power Line	
Church		Open Pit or Quarry	
Railroad		Lake (Blue)	
Hard Surfaced Road		Sand	
Improved Road		Marsh	
Unimproved Road		Woods	
Trail		River (Blue)	
Bridges		Hill Contour	

Topographic maps are always drawn with North at the top of map.

Black on the map indicates man-made features, such as buildings, roads, quarries, etc.

Blue on the map indicates water such as lakes, rivers, swamps, canals.

Green on the map indicates vegetation and trees.

Brown on the map indicates earth features, such as sand dunes, and the elevation. The brown contour lines show hills and valleys. If you trace around a heavy brown line with your finger, you will come to a number. This is the number of feet above sea level. A note in the margin of the map tells you the contour interval — the elevation in number of feet between the lines. Newer maps mark the contour in the metric system.

A topographic map tells you in the margin where True North is and where Magnetic North (see below) is. It also tells you the angle between these, which is called the angle of declination. This varies from place to place and year to year.

A topographic map often has a *grid system* of vertical and horizontal lines. This enables you to indicate a position on the map with great accuracy by referring to the grid numbers. The way in which the grid system is used is explained on the margin of the map.

Drawing a Sketch Map

When you are drawing a sketch map like the one of Treasure Island, you should draw it to scale. This means, for example, that if the distance between two roads is actually one kilometre and you make it five centimetres on your sketch map, everything else that is a kilometre apart should be five centimetres apart on your map.

The other thing to remember is to mark where North is. Most maps (and all topographic maps) are oriented so that North is at the top of the page. But you will find some maps that aren't so oriented. This is especially true of some city maps. When you are making a map, it is a good idea to put a 'compass rose' in the corner.

North

TRUE NORTH is where north really is — the very 'top' of the world when you remember that the world is a somewhat flattened globe, rotating on its axis. You can easily find True North on a

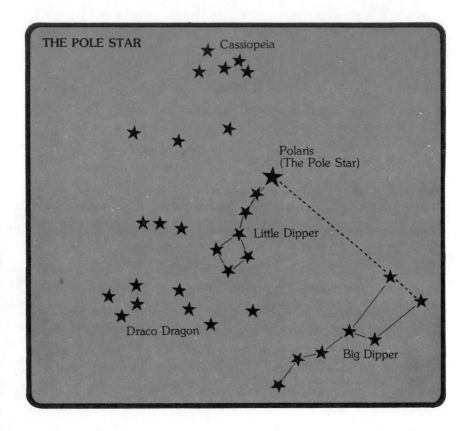

clear night. Find the Big Dipper (Ursa Major), one of the constellations that is always visible in Canada. The two stars on the outside of the dipper (not the handle) are the pointers. If you extend the line of the pointers for about five times the distance between these two stars, you will see a bright star. This is Polaris, the North Star. When you are facing it, you are facing True North.

MAGNETIC NORTH is where a compass points. A compass is a piece of steel which has been magnetized. When it is balanced on a point and left free to swing, it always comes to rest pointing in the same direction. This is because the planet Earth is like a magnet with one end in the north, and one in the south. The north end is somewhere north of Hudson Bay (and over 900 kilometres from true north). This magnetic north pole attracts your compass needle to it, and is what steadies it. Thus the end of your compass needle always points to Magnetic North, unless something interferes with the force of the attraction.

To Use a Compass

Remember to hold your compass flat. Hold it steady. Keep it away from objects containing iron which might attract the needle. Keep it away from power lines.

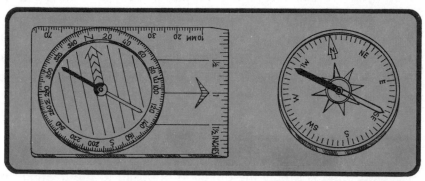

SILVA COMPASS   CONVENTIONAL COMPASS

Your compass needle will be in a 'housing' which has the four cardinal points (North, East, South, West) marked on it. It may also have the inter-cardinal points marked. To be really useful, it should be marked in degrees — a full circle or 360°.

To 'set' your compass, wait until the needle has come to rest (it always wavers slightly) and you will know that the coloured end is pointing to Magnetic North. Turn the housing slowly until 360° or N lies directly under the needle. Your compass is now 'set'.

Once you know where North is, you know where every other direction is because they never vary in their relationship to each other.

Using a Map with a Compass

Set the compass to the map by laying it on the map on a flat surface. Turn the map so that it agrees with your compass (which you have set first), that is, Magnetic North on the map is the same as North on your compass.

Taking a Bearing

This means finding out what direction a specific landmark is from where you are standing. For example, if you are standing at a corner and you want to know what direction a large tree in the distance is, you face the tree. Set your compass so that the coloured end of your needle lies over 360° or N. Sight across the level face of your compass so that you can see it and the tree. If it reads 90° you know it is due East.

Taking a Back-Bearing

A back-bearing is simply the direction opposite to the bearing. In the example given above, if you were to walk to the tree and wanted to get back to where you started you would go on the back-bearing, which is 270° or due West. (The back-bearing for 90° is 270°.)

If you were on 45° bearing, what would your back-bearing be?

If your bearing was 195° what would your back-bearing be?

Try these Map and Compass Activities

1. WALK A TRIANGLE Put a marker (coin, stone or something similar) on the ground at your feet. Set your compass. Face 60° and walk ten paces forward. Add 120° to your original bearing

— 180° — and walk ten paces in that direction. Add another 120° (300°), face that direction and walk another ten paces. If you were absolutely accurate, you will have returned to your original marker.

120° is one third of the complete 360° circle. Can you figure out a course which would let you walk a square?

2. MEASURING YOUR OWN PACE Everyone's pace is a different length and your own pace will vary as you grow older. A pace is a 'double-step'. If you start on your left foot, every time you put down your right foot, you have taken a pace. Now, figure out your average pace. Measure a distance of 100 metres. Walk it, using normal steps. Count each time your right foot touches the ground. Write down the total when you reach the end of the hundred metres. Walk back, counting again. Repeat this procedure again, so that you have walked the same hundred metres four times. Divide the total by four and you will know how many average paces it takes you to walk 100 metres. Try this exercise on smooth ground and rocky ground and find out if it makes a difference.

3. MEASURING THE DISTANCE BETWEEN TWO POINTS ON A MAP Take a piece of paper and compare it with the scale on the margin of a map. Make sure you start at the zero point on

the scale, which is not usually at the end of the scale line. Find two points with a hill between. What would be the shortest route? What would be the fastest route if you were on foot? Plot an imaginary hike on a map and figure out how far you would walk if you hiked the route.

4. SET A COMPASS TRAIL Setting a compass trail for a friend to follow is fun. Make sure you are absolutely accurate. It helps to be accurate if you have someone taking back-bearings for you. Leaving messages or objects at various points on the trail adds to the fun.

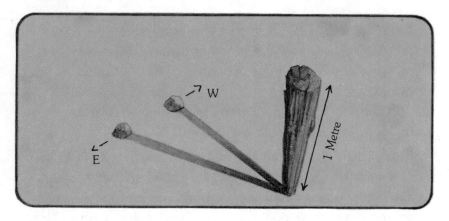

5. FIND NORTH BY THE SUN Some sunny morning plant a stick upright in the ground. Mark the end of the shadow cast by the stick. Continue marking the end of the shadow as it moves, over the next few hours. A line joining these marks will be an east-west line. The stick will cast its shortest shadow at noon (Standard Time) because the sun is then almost directly overhead. Since the sun rises in the east and sets in the west, you will know which end of your line is east.

6. FINDING DIRECTION BY A WRIST WATCH Lay the watch flat on the ground, with the hour hand pointing at the sun. Check this by placing a very thin stick or match upright at the edge of the watch where the hour hand is pointing. The

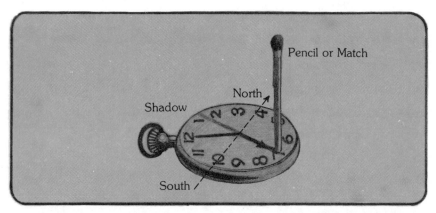

shadow should fall along the hour hand. If it doesn't, turn the watch until it does. (If you are on Daylight Saving time, turn your watch *back* an hour first. When getting direction from the sun, you must be on Standard, i.e. sun time.) Halfway between the hour hand and twelve o'clock on the dial is true *South*. Mark a line on the ground to indicate your north-south line.

This method will work between 6 a.m. and 6 p.m. (Standard Time) — as long as you can see the sun. Before 6 a.m. and after 6 p.m., halfway between the hour hand and twelve o'clock will be North.

Boating

Did you know that a lot of Canada's surface is water? And that Canada is bounded by three oceans? That makes us a very water-conscious people. In its early years, Canada's 'roads' were its lakes and rivers. Today, most of us use those same lakes and rivers for swimming and boating. If you boat, you should be able to swim. And whether or not you are a good swimmer, you should know the safety rules concerning boating.

(i)   Wear a government-approved lifejacket.

(ii) Carry a bailer, oars, and an extra lifejacket in boats.

(iii) Stay with the boat if it overturns; it will help keep you afloat.

(iv) Don't overload a boat.

(v) Know how to stay afloat by treading water or drownproofing.

(vi) Know how to give artificial respiration by rescue breathing and another method.

Jenny dawdled as she neared home one win'ry day. The wind, blowing up swirls of snow, stung her face, but her curiosity overcame her discomfort. There was a moving van outside the house next door. Jenny watched the furniture being moved in and wondered if someone her age would live there. It was hard to tell. The small two-wheeler meant a little kid and that would make her little sister happy.

"Mum!" she hollered as soon as she had shut the door. Her mother's voice came faintly from the basement. She was in the workshop, as usual these days, refinishing some old furniture she had bought at auction sales. Her father used to tease her mother about her bargains, but since she had started teaching furniture refinishing at night school, he had suddenly begun boasting about her 'finds'.

"Mum, is that ever nice! Who would've thought that old rocking chair could look that good!" Jenny admired her mother's handiwork. Lately she had often helped with the sanding and polishing and knew how much hard work went into it. "Somebody's moving in next door. The van's there. Have you seen it? Do you know if there are any girls my age?"

"I've been down here almost all day, Jen," her mother answered. "I just lose track of time when I'm doing this. It's a miserable day for anyone to be moving. I can tell that, even from the basement window."

"Would it look too nosy if I just went and asked?"

"Probably." Jenny's face fell, so her mother added, "Look — I took a pie out of the freezer for dinner before I started this. We don't really need dessert, or I can open a can of fruit. Why don't you take the pie around and introduce yourself?"

Jenny held the pie carefully as she knocked on their new neighbour's door. A pleasant-looking woman answered.

"Hi! I'm Jenny Evans and I live next door. My mum thought you might like to have a pie for dinner." Not knowing what to make of the look of suprise on the woman's face, she added, "My mum's a really good cook. Especially pies."

"Well, that's awfully nice of her. I haven't given dinner a thought but I know we'll enjoy this. We've moved lots of times, but nobody's ever brought us a pie before. I have a daughter about your age. Everything's in an awful mess, but come and meet her. She's in the living room sorting out our pictures for the walls."

That evening, Jenny phoned Carol to tell her about her new neighbour. "You'll see her at school tomorrow, Carol. Her name's Chris, and she'll be in our grade, and she's in a wheel chair. That's why they moved to our neighbourhood; because our school has hardly any stairs. It's really sharp. She showed me how it works."

"I wouldn't like being in a wheel chair," said Carol.

"What I mean is, if you can't walk by yourself, it's really neat the way it works and how she can run it herself. You know what I mean."

"What happened to her?"

"She was in a really bad car accident. She just told me a little bit about it. It happened when she was seven, and her aunt was killed. Anyhow, she probably won't ever be able to walk again. She can swim though, and do all sorts of things. She won a horseshoe tournament last summer, and d'you know what? She's a Guide!"

Although the school had few steps, the church hall in which the Guides met had more. Because the outside snow-covered steps were slippery Chris's father brought her to Guides.

Jenny and Carol were anxious to have her in the Daffodil Patrol and when Chris said that's where she'd like to be, they were elated. Mrs. Mac told Chris she could decide later which patrol she'd like to be in permanently. "Why don't you wait a couple of weeks and then decide? By then, you'll know more of the girls."

Jenny and three other girls were busily planning a party. "If you want to help us, Chris, you can. It's a January party for the people at the nursing home. We were going to have a Christmas party with them, but they were already having several parties then, so we decided to have a January one instead. We're going to bake cookies at my house and they'll let us make tea and coffee there."

"What are you going to do at the party besides eat?" asked Chris.

"That's what we have to talk about tonight," said Nancy. "My grandmother lives at the nursing home and when Jenny and I went to visit her last Saturday we talked about what we could do. A lot of the people like playing things like bingo, cards and

checkers; so we'll play games part of the time. We're making little prizes."

"I know how to make bath salts that don't cost much money," said Chris. "If you put some in fancy bottles, they look really nice. We made some in my last Guide company for gifts."

"That's a good idea. And another thing we're going to do is kinda funny to do at a party. The lady in my grandmother's room is really good at crocheting. She makes millions of squares for afghans and she's going to teach us how. Actually, three ladies are going to teach us. It will be sort of a competition to see who learns the fastest. It was her idea to have a competition. Everyone else is going to watch."

"Tell her what that funny old man said — the one who used to be a cowboy and likes to tell you all about the times he almost got killed. He's over ninety and you should hear the adventures he's had!"

"My grandmother was a bit cross with him. He said he was going to get people to bet on us like race horses and my grandmother said if he did, she wouldn't let him come to the party. We were beginning to wonder whose party it was!"

"I've never been to a nursing home," said Chris. "What's it like?"

"Well, everyone there is old and can't look after themselves, or haven't anyone to look after them. Some people never have any visitors to talk to. The director of the nursing home told us they really enjoy having young people like us coming to see them, because they hardly ever see anybody young. It was a bit hard getting used to some of them, because some like to touch you a lot and some have lost their memories and say funny things."

"One lady kept calling me Maude," said Jenny. "She thought I was somebody she knew when she was young. She'd get mad at me for something the real Maude did and that bothered me until Nancy's grandmother explained about her.

"And Chris, it'll be easy for you to go because there's ramps for wheel chairs. The whole building was planned to make it easy for people in wheel chairs to get around, just like the new auditorium downtown."

"We're going to sing, too," said Nancy. "We're going to sing some Guide songs, and we're going to sing some of their favourite songs. We've been practising them because most of the old people have shaky voices when they sing. At my house the other night we learned some old songs. There is a really funny one called 'School Days'. My mother has a book of songs that belonged to my grandmother and she played them on the piano for us."

"Hey!" said Kim. "we've just about got the whole party planned, by telling Chris about it. Let's write it all down. Then we can tell if we need anything else and decide who's going to bring stuff."

Mrs. Mac wandered over to the corner where the girls were planning. "Hi," she said. "How are your plans coming? Are you going to help with the January party they're putting on, Chris?"

"We're just going to write down our plans," said Jenny. "You want to help us, don't you Chris? Could we get our Hostess Badge when we're finished?"

"I've already got my Hostess Badge," said Chris. "I helped put on a Hallowe'en party last year. I told a spooky ghost story and we had a taped background of weird noises. We really had fun! But I'd still like to help with the January party. I was working on my Baker Badge before we moved, and maybe I could make butter tarts. I'm learning how."

"How do you roll out pastry in a wheel chair?" asked Kim, and then wished she hadn't asked, in case it made Chris feel bad. But Chris didn't seem to mind at all.

"No problem," she answered. "My dad made a cutting board that fits across my wheel chair, just for things like that. It fastens on the sides. He actually made two. I use one just for food.

"I like cooking, and it's not bad doing it in a wheel chair. Look you guys, don't be afraid to ask how I do things. I'd rather tell you than have you wonder, or even worse, treat me as if I couldn't do something. There's lots I can't do, but there's lots more I can do."

Jenny took a deep breath and plunged into the opening Chris had given her, with a question she'd been wondering about since their first meeting. "Chris, what does it feel like — I mean, well when people see you, they kinda . . ." her voice trailed off miserably.

"Stare at me, you mean?" said Chris quietly. "I'm used to it. In a way, I guess I'll never really be used to it. But I know that people do it, and there's no way I can stop them. That's what I keep telling myself. And it's funny — when *I* see somebody who looks different, I find myself staring at them! Anyhow, when I see some-body staring at me I try to smile and say 'Hello'. That embarrasses some people, and they try to pretend they haven't been looking at me at all.

"I was in the hospital for a long time, and that's where I learned to do lots and lots of things. I was bad for a while because I got pretty spoiled. My uncle — he was driving when the accident happened — kept bringing me expensive presents and I thought I could have anything I wanted. It wasn't his fault at all. The other driver was drunk, really smashed.

At first I wouldn't try to do things I should. But after a while it got pretty boring, so when nobody was looking I used to do stuff I had said I couldn't. Then I guess I just decided that I'd be a lot happier trying, so I did.

What I really hate is when people feel sorry for me. One friend of my mother's always called me 'poor little thing' and I just hated it. Her kids are all champion athletes. Sometimes I heard her talking to my mother about me when they didn't know I was listening. One day my mother got mad at her and told her off. It was the same day I'd baked my first batch of shortbread — I was only nine. After my mother sort of cooled off, she called me from my room and asked me to serve the shortbread I'd just made."

"I bet that made her change her mind about you," said Jenny. "What did she say when she tasted it?"

Chris laughed at the memory. "She hated being wrong about anything. She just smiled at me. I didn't really know what it was all about, just that my mother had got mad. Then she said to my mother, 'Isn't it fortunate that Christine has inherited her father's long arms!' It seemed a stupid thing to say, and for days I used to look at my arms to see if they were longer than other kids' or not. They aren't. And neither are my dad's; in fact, his arms are short for his height!"

Mrs. Mac had been sitting listening while Chris talked. "If you catch any of us feeling sorry for you, Chris, just tell us you've got extra long arms and we'll remember to watch out!" She looked at her watch. "The Robin Patrol has a game they'd like everyone to play. Can you wind things up in five minutes and come when the whistle blows?"

The Robins always had good games. They had old recipe file cards in their patrol box with written directions for games they liked. They were good at giving new twists to old games, too.

Jane, the Robin Patrol Leader, said, "This game is called 'Wax Museum'. Remember the wax museum we went to on our trip last fall and how they had groups of people made from wax that looked real enough to be alive?"

Everyone remembered it, especially the Chamber of Horrors. Jane continued, "We've got a slip of paper for each patrol. It says what you're supposed to be. They're all groups of people doing something. You've got to pretend you're all made of wax. Take five minutes to plan and practise in your patrol corner how you're going to make up the scene.

"When I blow my whistle, come to this end of the hall and one patrol at a time will get in position. Remember you're made of wax, so you can't move a muscle. We'll judge the best scene and take off points if we see anyone move. Any questions?"

When they got back to their patrol corner, the Daffodils looked at their slip. It read, 'You are a group of women in Manitoba in 1915 taking part in a demonstration to demand that women be allowed to vote in provincial elections.' Their preparation time was soon up, but they even had a paper banner reading 'Women Want the Vote!' which Lynn held steadily aloft after they had taken up their positions.

The Fireweed Patrol won. There was no doubt that their grouping of 'People at the start of the Polar Bear Swim on January 1st' was the best. They even managed to look as if they were shivering although they apparently didn't move a muscle.

When Jenny got home from Guides that night, the house was in a turmoil. Her Aunt Joan was talking to her mother, her little sister was rocking her ten-month-old cousin, Mark, in his carriage, and her father was trying to entertain the almost-four-year-old twins, Sean and Cheryl.

"Oh hi, Jenny!" said Aunt Joan, looking up. "Do they teach you anything about looking after children in Guides? Your mum has just agreed to take on these three for a couple of weeks."

Jenny's face lit up. "Really? You mean they're all gonna stay here, at our house. That's super!" She turned to her mother. "Maybe I can stay home from school, Mum, and help look after them."

"Trust you to think of that, Jenny" said her mother. "I think I can manage while you're at school. Aunt Joan has to go to her mother-in-law's. She's just been sent home from hospital and there's nobody to look after her until she's strong enough to be on her own again. They don't allow children to stay in her apartment building. Aunt Joan's flying out there first thing in the morning; that's why she drove down here tonight."

"Where's everybody going to sleep?" asked Jenny. "I can put my sleeping bag on the floor and it'll be just like being at camp."

Next day after school, Carol and Kim went home with Jenny.

"When I told my mum about your cousins," said Kim, "she said your mother's brave. The idea of twins scares her. I've got one cousin who's four and one of him is enough for anybody. You should see what he gets into!"

Sean and Cheryl aren't like that — well, not usually, just sometimes. I'm glad they're not identical twins like those guys in the other grade seven class. They can really think up ways to trick people!"

"I think it'd be great to have a twin," said Carol. "I used to wish I had an identical twin brother, but my mother told me that's impossible. I mean outside of the fact that I wasn't a twin to begin with. You have to be the same sex to be identical twins.

"What d'you mean, impossible?" asked Kim. "If you had the same haircut and everything, you'd be identical. Well almost; I mean he'd be a boy and you'd be a girl."

"Uh-uh," said Carol, shaking her head. "You know all the stuff about a male sperm fertilizing the female egg cell and the egg developing into a baby? Well, sometimes a woman has two egg cells at the same time from her ovaries and both get fertilized. That's when you get twins that aren't identical; they're just like two brothers, or two sisters, or a sister and brother. I think you call them fraternal twins.

"But sometimes the one egg that a woman usually has at a time splits in two — or even more — when it's fertilized and that's when you get identical twins or triplets. They have to be the same sex if they started out as one fertilized egg cell. It's really interesting. I'm going to do a project on genetics for the Science Fair."

"I know," said Jenny. "When my Aunt Joan was pregnant last time she was afraid she was going to have twins again. She adores the twins and they're really sweet kids, but it's a lot of work when they're babies, with all the diapers and bottles and everything. Have you ever seen anything being born?"

"I almost saw puppies once," said Kim. "Before we moved to the townhouse where we live now — they won't let us have dogs there and I think it's mean — we had a dog who had puppies. But she had them when I was at school."

"Once I saw a calf being born at my grandfather's farm," said Carol. "You should have seen it. You can hardly believe it's really going to happen. I mean it's almost unbelievable that something as big as a baby can come out of an opening so small in the mother. And then the opening gets small again. Like putting your head through a turtleneck sweater!

"My grandfather said it always makes him sure that God's for real. He says that even if scientists figure out a way to make babies in test tubes, it won't be half as wonderful as the natural way. D'you know how long an elephant's pregnant? Over a year and a half!"

"Here come the twins!" Jenny laughed as Sean and Cheryl grabbed her hands and started talking at the same time.

"Take us to the park, take us to the park! We can take our sled."

"O.K., but you have to wait for us to put our books in the house. This is my friend, Carol and my friend, Kim."

Sean looked at the girls solemnly before saying, "I like friends."

After an hour on the snow-covered slopes at the park, the twins were rosy-cheeked and bouncing with happiness. The girls were beginning to feel weary and looked thankfully at the darkening sky.

Jenny was adamant. "Cheryl, just one last ride down the hill. It's getting dark. And no more making angels in the snow. You're almost soaked through now. We have to get you home and warm you up."

Back at Jenny's house, they found Chris in the living room, playing with baby Mark.

"Hi," she said. "My mother brought me over. I thought maybe your mum would appreciate a baby-sitter while she got dinner and I knew you guys had gone to the park with the twins. And guess what? I changed him."

Carol and Kim said good-bye reluctantly and promised Sean and Cheryl that they'd come after school the next day. Supper was a bit of an adventure. Chris looked after Mark. Mrs. Evans had borrowed a high chair and Chris sat beside it in her wheel chair. She had to duck as the baby's hands tried to pull her hair with fingers dipped in applesauce. "He needs a bib," she said, "but I need a raincoat!"

Cheryl looked daringly at Jenny. "I don't eat dinner. I don't like it."

Sean, who had already dug into his dinner with gusto, put his spoon down. "Me don't eat dinner, too," he announced, and slid off his chair.

Jenny looked at her mother in despair. "Do they have to? What should I do?"

Her mother picked up Sean firmly and set him on his chair. "Tell us about the park, Sean. What did you do?"

"Me went down big hill with Jenny." He started to get excited and absent-mindedly picked up his spoon and began eating again.

"It was a great big hill, wasn't it, Sean? And tomorrow we can go again. If you're still strong enough." Jenny watched Cheryl out of the corner of her eye. "I think you'll be strong enough, Sean — look at how you're eating your dinner! One of these days you'll even be strong enough to pull the sled up the big hill!"

"Me, too," said Cheryl suddenly. "I'll be strong enough, too." She started to eat her dinner. Jenny heaved a sigh of relief.

For the next two weeks, Jenny and usually Carol, Chris and Kim played with Jenny's cousins after school. Aunt Joan had brought a few of their favourite toys for them to play with, but the twins looked forward to playing with those that the girls made out of paper, boxes, bags and almost any odds and ends they could find.

The most exciting day was when baby Mark took his first steps. He had been pulling himself up at the side of Chris's wheel chair, watching her do fingerplays for him. He became so entranced that he let go and walked toward the front of the chair without holding on.

"I wish I could learn to walk away from this wheel chair," said Chris somewhat regretfully. Mark caught the note of sadness in her voice and sat down with a bump. Chris laughed at him. "Up again, Mark! Even if I can't walk, I've helped you to!"

The house seemed terribly empty after Aunt Joan returned and took the children home. A sudden thaw came, removing most of the snow and bringing rain and bone-chilling weather. Jenny was just getting ready for bed on one such evening when Lynn telephoned her.

"Jenny, I'm phoning all the patrol. Carol's line is busy, so can you tell her tomorrow? You two walk to school together, don't you?"

"Sure, Lynn. Tell her what? What's it about?"

"Well, you know that some of us who are working on our Citizen Badge went to the town council meeting tonight. Cathy — she's a Ranger but she was probably still in Guides when you first joined — took us, because a bunch of people from her street were going. The first part of the meeting was pretty boring, and we had trouble figuring out what they were talking about half the time. One man on the council was smart-alecky sometimes. If I had been the mayor, I'd have told him where to get off.

"Anyhow, they finally got to the part that Cathy's neighbours had come for. They'd written a letter complaining about the trash and junk along the river. The street Cathy lives on ends at the river, and all the kids who live down that way play along the edge of the river."

"I know where you mean," interrupted Jenny. "I had a friend who lived near there and my mum didn't like me playing there, because of so much broken glass and even rusty bits of old cars and . . ."

"Yeah, well, it's got worse and worse. They were supposed to clean it up and put in a park or playground, but they changed their minds. Usually the town does clean it up a bit — gets rid of the big hunks of garbage anyhow — but last fall, the snow came so early and heavily that it never got done. And the other day, when the first thaw came and the kids were still trying to sleigh ride down some little hills there, the snow didn't cover all the junk anymore. There was a broken television aerial and a little kid fell on it and rammed one of the metal ends down her throat."

"Yikes!" exclaimed Jenny. "That sounds terrible! What did they do?"

"Not too much. You can't put a bandage on the roof of your mouth. She got a tetanus shot and painkiller and antibiotics, but I guess it was pretty awful for her for a few days. It's healing quickly, but her parents and all the neighbours were pretty upset because it's such a junk yard down there and it could be nice."

"I don't blame them for being upset. But it's fun playing down there."

"Anyhow, they wrote a letter telling the mayor and council about the accident and blamed the town for not having kept the riverside cleaner. They said if it looks like a junk yard, people will use it for one.

The council wasn't very happy. You should have heard them argue! One man on the council said parents shouldn't let their kids play down there. Then somebody said the closest park was two miles away. One of the councillors said she'd been trying to get the town to budget for the river's regular clean-up ever since she'd been elected to the council. Then they got talking about how much sewers and road repairs cost and what they could or couldn't afford.''

"Didn't anybody care about the little kid who got hurt, or the kids not having a place to play, or the river's edge looking a mess?" asked Jenny.

"This one man sure didn't. He pounded his desk and said he wasn't going to raise the taxes just so spoiled kids, whose parents wouldn't look after them around the home, could wreck expensive playground equipment. I got the feeling he didn't like kids much.

"But most of the others were pretty good. And they all felt badly about the little girl being hurt. The mayor got everyone settled down — Cathy's neighbours were mad too, and everybody started to shout. It was practically like a fight in the schoolyard; I never saw grown-ups act like that before, not in public. The mayor threatened to clear the chambers — that means kick everybody out — and everyone simmered down.

"He said he thought the people who lived around the river had some responsibility for keeping the riverside clean even if they weren't the ones who dumped the garbage there. Everyone didn't agree with that — they said it was public property and the public's taxes should pay for it. It ended when they decided to give it serious thought. I don't know if that means they're going to *do* anything about it. It sounds like when your parents say 'wait and see'.''

"Was that all?''

"Then Cathy drove us home — she's got her driver's permit now — and she told us about this idea she had. She wants the Rangers and the Guides — the other Guide companies in town, too

— to get together and do something about the river clean-up While the town council is giving it serious thought, we can give it serious work and maybe then the town will know some people really do care. She's going to ask the Boy Scouts and Venturers, too."

"You mean we'd all get together and just go down and collect garbage? When? Suppose it snows again? It's still winter."

"It probably won't snow before Saturday and if we get as many kids as we can for this Saturday, they'll know we mean action."

"What'll we do with all the stuff?" Jenny was doubtful. It seemed a gigantic undertaking.

"That's easy. One of Cathy's neighbours has a truck and he was there. He said he was free on Saturday and would drive back and forth to the dump. Cathy's father is going to see if he can get cardboard cartons at work and so will one of the women who was there. We figure that's better than plastic garbage bags. They cost money and they aren't biodegradable and anyhow, these are big strong cartons. If we had a lot of kids, we could get a lot done." Lynn paused dramatically, and added, "It could have been one of those cute little cousins of yours who got a piece of TV aerial down her throat."

"Oh Lynn, you didn't have to say that! I was going to say yes. And I'll tell Carol. What time is it going to be?"

"Nine-thirty Saturday morning. We'll meet at the corner of Riverside and Queen Streets. Bring extra mitts or gloves and wear old clothes."

"Do we bring our lunch?"

"Didn't I tell you?" asked Lynn in a saving-the-best-for-the-last sort of voice. "The parents of the little girl who was hurt happen to own a restaurant, and they're going to bring us hamburgers and chips and shakes at noon. Free!"

"Why didn't you say so before?" demanded Jenny.

"And bribe you? Not me!" said Lynn. "You know I wouldn't bribe you if I didn't have to. And I didn't have to, did I?"

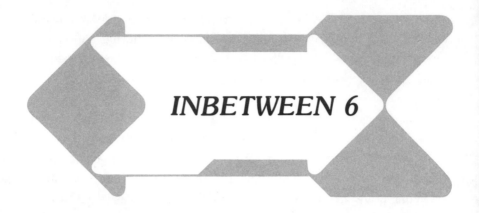

INBETWEEN 6

GOING ONCE — GOING TWICE — GONE!

Have you ever been to an auction sale? It's a lot of fun even if you don't buy anything. Dealers in antiques, and people who are serious collectors, know a great deal about old things — furniture, glassware, silver, metals, books, prints, pottery. They may know, for example, just where the factory once existed that made what looks to you like a faded, worn-out plate. Remember the Crystal Palace where the first Scout Rally was held, the one the girls gate-crashed? You might find a print of the Crystal Palace at an auction sale. There's a well known one of Queen Victoria and Prince Albert opening an exhibition there, long before the 1909 Rally, or course, but it shows you what a grand building it was.

Do you collect anything? Some people get started on collections when they buy something that appeals to them at an auction sale. It might be anything from an old key to a rocking chair, from a school bell to a school book, from a tin tray with advertising on it to china with famous people's portraits! Whatever you collect, if a lot of people are interested in the same thing, the item will become scarce and the price go up. That's fine if you are the seller but disappointing if you're the buyer!

Whatever you collect, and whether it's old and scarce or new and more common, you will enjoy your collection more if you display it attractively. Also finding out all you can about your collection adds interest. Some kinds of collections are best kept in a scrapbook or album. For example, there are special ways to keep and mount postage stamps in albums.

Shelves are useful for collections of larger objects. If you haven't any, save your money and build your own with planks and bricks or cement blocks, or use thinner wood and wall-mounted brackets. Small objects can be displayed in a partitioned shadow box which you can make from a sturdy carton. Paint it with rubber base paint and use a contrasting colour for the inside.

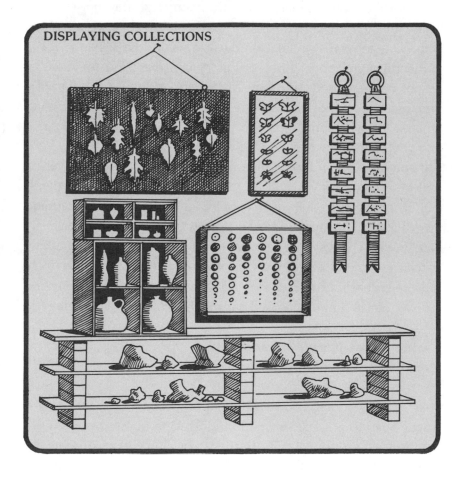

DISPLAYING COLLECTIONS

Some things can be mounted and framed, or attached to burlap-covered corrugated cardboard and displayed on the wall.

Whatever you collect, it will reflect your interests. It may become a lifetime pleasure and hobby.

HELPING THE HANDICAPPED

Almost everybody has some sort of handicap. Many handicaps are so minor that you can easily adapt to them and may not even be aware that you have them. Some are much greater and mean that you have to make a lot of adjustments in daily living. It's a tremendous challenge, for example, if you are blind, or deaf, or cannot walk unaided, or if you see words on the page differently from most people, or have severe breathing problems, or have lost an arm. It's a challenge because you still want to learn, to do, and to enjoy what others do. And it's harder.

If you have a handicap which seems to prevent you from taking part in a Guide activity, talk to your Guider. Badge requirements can be changed to suit *your* capabilities, as long as the requirement fulfills the purpose behind the badge and isn't too easy for you. Suggest ways that will help you join in normal company activities; you probably know your own limitations. And you might surprise yourself. Lord Baden-Powell used to talk about "knocking the 'im' out of 'impossible'." That's a challenge for everyone!

Caring about people's handicaps
How does your community rate?

Take a look around your community, especially at buildings and places open to anyone. Answer the following questions by checking the 'yes' or 'no' column. Perhaps you'd like to give points for all the 'yes' answers. Can you think of other questions to ask?

	YES	NO
If your public library has stairs, does it also have a ramp?		
Does your library have a good selection of large-print books?		
Do your theatres and auditoriums have wheel chair accommodation?		
Do most stores have entrances suitable for wheel chair users, and aisles of sufficient width?		
Is there a public telephone which a person in a wheel chair or on crutches could easily use?		
Are bus, streetcar and taxi drivers generally patient and understanding with handicapped passengers, including the elderly?		
Are street signs easy to read and well-lit at night?		
Are sidewalks smooth and are curbs kept in good repair?		
Do major intersections have traffic lights which indicate when it is safe to walk?		
Would a student in a wheel chair find it easy to get around in your school?		
Are staircases and entranceways where your Guide company meets well lit?		
Do staircases in all public buildings have sturdy handrails?		
Do most churches have entrances suitable for wheel chair users?		
Do bathrooms in public buildings have doorways wide enough for wheel chairs?		

	YES	NO
Are any churches or auditoriums equipped with earphones for the hard-of-hearing?		
If you have a swimming instruction programme in your community, does it include instruction for handicapped adults?		
Does your school system have special classes for children with learning handicaps?		
Is there sufficient opportunity for employment for mentally handicapped adults?		
Could a person in a wheel chair easily visit a friend in hospital?		

Make friends with some senior citizens

There was once a Guide who went with her company to put on a Valentine Tea in a nursing home. On the way home, she announced very firmly that she was never going to be old and bedridden, that she would "die first"! She was a very pretty Guide and her own grandmothers were active, young-looking and attractive. The old people in the nursing home were the first old people she had ever met who were ailing, forgetful, and not very happy. It can come as a shock, if you've never known an old person, to discover what aging does to some people. Sometimes it's because others haven't cared enough about what happens to the elderly that they become bed-ridden, or unhappy.

This particular Guide vowed she'd never go and visit old people again, and she didn't. Other Guides tried to talk her out of it but they couldn't. They thought her Promise and Law didn't mean much to her if she wouldn't even *try* to cope with her fear of being old (and not beautiful) some day.

In his last message to the Guides of the world, B-P wrote, "Your business in life is to be happy and to make others happy. You begin making other people happy by doing good turns for them. You need not worry about making yourselves happy, as you will very soon find that that comes by itself: when you make other people happy, it makes you happy too."

Here are some things you can do to bring happiness to senior citizens, many of whom are lonely, where you live. Some you can do alone, some are suitable for patrols or the whole company to do together.

— Visit older people, especially those without families nearby, and who often have very few young visitors. They get weary of seeing only old people all the time!

— Offer your services to carry messages, shop, clean, shovel snow, rake leaves, read for those whose sight has failed, or get books from the library.

— Visit senior citizens and nursing homes. Play games, like checkers and bingo, with them. Have a singsong. Take some treats, but find out first what is acceptable. Many elderly people are on special or sugar-free diets.

— Remember their birthdays and other special occasions with greeting cards.

— Be patient. The elderly may speak and think slowly. They may repeat what they have already told you several times over.

— Many older people have no means of transportation and sometimes haven't seen their city or countryside for many years. Enlist willing parents who drive, to help you with tours of autumn leaves, spring blossoms, Christmas lights or just new developments around the community.

— Active senior citizens may enjoy doing something for *you*. Learn a skill from a senior citizen — quilting, bread making, even dancing the Charleston!

— If you want to find out what it was like going to school seventy or eighty years ago, ask a senior citizen. They will have many interesting stories.

— Don't be a nuisance. You've probably heard the old joke about the Boy Scout who was late for his Scout meeting. When the Scouter asked why, he said he had been trying to do a good turn. He was helping an old lady across the street, but she didn't want to go!

— Is there a Meals-on-Wheels service in your community? If so, they often appreciate little extras, like fancy cookies, for the meals they take to elderly people. And at holiday times especially, they might appreciate older Guides to help as 'runners' for the volunteers who drive the meals around.

— Many community service groups do things for those in need at times like Christmas, but not during other times of the year. Perhaps Guides could be of better service, if they remembered those times of year when others forget...

COOKIE RECIPES

"What's blue and covered with crumbs?"
"A Girl Guide who fell into her cookies on Cookie Day!"

It's a pretty corny joke, but a lot of people think of cookie selling when they think of Girl Guides. Guiding in Canada couldn't get along without its wonderful cookie saleswomen, but we wish the public would notice the other things we can do, too.

Still, there's something yummy about cookies, especially when you make them yourself. Try these cookie recipes and *give* some away.

Monster Munch

1-1/2 cups chocolate chips
3 crushed Shredded Wheat biscuits
1 cup coconut
1/2 cup crushed peanuts

Melt the chocolate chips in the top of a double boiler. Add the other ingredients. Mix well. Drop by the spoonful on a waxed paper-covered cookie sheet. Chill.

Peanut Butter Chocolate Chip Cookies à la Doe Lake

1 cup sifted all-purpose flour
1/3 cup margarine, butter or shortening
1 cup white sugar
2 eggs
1 6-ounce package chocolate chips (170g)
1 tsp. baking powder
1/4 tsp. salt
1/2 cup peanut butter
1/2 tsp. vanilla
1/4 cup firmly packed brown sugar

Preheat oven to 350°.
Beat butter and peanut butter until smooth and well-blended. Add sugars and beat until light. Add eggs and continue beating until fluffy. Sift the dry ingredients, add gradually and beat until smooth. Add chocolate chips and vanilla. Spoon batter into greased 9" square pan, spreading evenly. Bake for 25 minutes or until done. Cool and cut into squares.

Janelle's Simple Cookies

1/2 cup white sugar
1/2 cup corn syrup
1/2 cup peanut butter
flaked breakfast cereal

Bring sugar and syrup to a boil. Remove from stove and add peanut butter. Mix in enough cereal to make a stiff dough. Drop on greased cookie sheet by the spoonful. Let set.

Canadian Centennial Squares

1/4 lb. butter
1 cup graham cracker crumbs
1 cup coconut
6 oz. crushed nuts (170g)
6 oz. chocolate chips (170g)
1 14 oz. can sweetened condensed milk (397g)

Melt butter in 9" square pan. Sprinkle crumbs over butter. Sprinkle coconut over crumbs. Sprinkle chocolate chips, then nuts. Pour condensed milk on top. DO NOT STIR. Bake at 350° for 25 min. Cool and cut.

HAVE A PARTY!

HAVE A BALL!
BE THE HOSTESS WITH THE MOSTEST!

Guides always enjoy doing the Hostess Badge. Putting on a party is a lot of work and a lot of fun. Get a group together and put on a party.

Your party could be for the other Guides in your company, on all sorts of occasions. Hallowe'en? Christmas? Valentine's? St. Patrick's? April Fool's? Welcome Spring? Au Revoir to a friend who is moving? A Just Because Party?

It could be for another Guide company or a Brownie pack or a Ranger/Cadet group. Thinking Day? Sports Party? Swim Party? Barbecue? Guides Alive Party?

It could be for girls whom you'd like to interest in Guides. Fun and Frolic Party? Masquerade? Any of the above Parties?

It could be for mothers, fathers, people who have helped your company, senior citizens, little children — almost anyone, in fact!

Open House? Picnic in the Park? Formal Tea? Party with an international flavour? Coffee-house style party? Birthday Party? Unbirthday Party?

The choice is yours!

When you know who your guests are, and what the theme of the party will be, the planning gets exciting. Here are some questions to ask yourselves.

(i)   How many guests will there be?

(ii) How will we greet them?

> Hi there!
>
> You're invited to my
> Halloween party,
> on Fri., October 31, 6 pm.
> at my house,
> 88 Glenway Drive, no. 16
>
> Hope you can come,
> see you then,
> in your costume!
>
> Sally Nealson
>
> R.S.V.P.
> 723-4851

(iii)   What's the date and the time?

(iv)   Will we make formal or informal invitations?

(v)   How long ahead shall we send the invitations?

(vi)   How will we arrange the room so that everyone is comfortable?

(vii)   What will we do at the party?
Games? Make a list and assign one game to each hostess.
Prizes? Music? Will we have records, or singing, or instruments, or all three?

(viii)   What will we eat?
Who will prepare the food? Who will buy it? How will we pay for it?

(ix)   Will we have decorations? Who will get them? When will we put them up?

(x)   How will we bid good-bye to our guests?

(xi)   How will we divide the clean-up jobs evenly?

IF THE PARTY'S FUN, THE GUESTS WILL BE HAPPY
. . . . . IF THE GUESTS ARE HAPPY, THE PARTY WILL BE FUN!

Small courtesies create good feelings

When you have been invited to a party, you have an obligation to help the party go well, too. It isn't just up to the hostess.
Try to be:

— enthusiastic (but not rowdy).

—co-operative (you might not like all the games, but if you join in whole-heartedly, they'll be more fun).

One of the little things in life that gives other people a lift, is receiving thank you notes — for gifts, for a good time, for their hospitality to you. It's a good habit to have. Lord Baden-Powell once said, "A gift isn't yours until you've said thank you."

Although any kind of thank you note is appreciated, it's nice to take special care with it. Use proper notepaper if possible. Use a pen. Pencil fades, and the recipient might want to treasure your letter for a long time! Try not to make spelling or grammatical mistakes. If spelling isn't your thing, use a dictionary. Remember margins and your address and the date. When you sign your letter, use only your first name unless the person to whom you are writing doesn't know you very well. In that case, include your surname and not just your last initial.

If you have been invited to a party, it's courteous to let the hostess know if you can come. Sometimes you may see R.S.V.P. on an invitation. It stands for 'répondez s'il vous plâit', which is French for 'please reply'. If you have to decline an invitation, word it carefully. Don't make it sound as if you didn't want to come!

ENTERTAINING SMALL CHILDREN

One of the secrets of providing fun and happiness for little children is to use your own imagination. They are always eager and interested in seeing and doing something new. Even the child who is kicking and screaming because his mother has gone out and left him in your care can be gently won over. But *gently* does it.

Remember the paper dolls in the introduction to this book? If you pretend to ignore the child's screams, and slowly start cutting out a series of paper dolls, talking as if to yourself about what you're doing, the child will almost certainly be overcome by curiosity to see what you're doing. Children are curious; you can be sure of that! If the dolls don't work, try trees or houses and by then he's almost certain to be won over.

Make a Baby-sitter's Bag...ideas you can use to amuse; bits of no-cost or low-cost equipment you keep just to take with you when looking after preschoolers.

Try These

Paper Folding Make a paper hat. Make a paper airplane. Make a paper puppet from half an envelope. Make a paper cup that you can really drink from. If you attach a ball of crumpled paper to the paper cup with a piece of wool, you have a game in which you try to toss the ball in the cup. Make the cup larger, turn it upside down, and you have a different style of hat. If you really want to

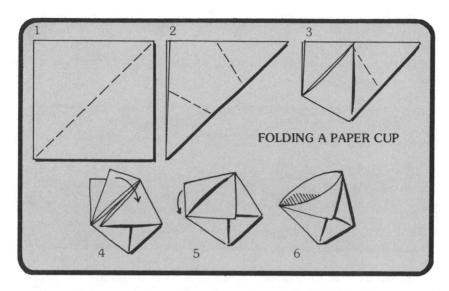

FOLDING A PAPER CUP

acquire paper-folding skills, look in the library for a book on origami, the Japanese art of paper folding. Then learn how to make a bird which flaps its wings when you pull its tail — a crane!

Cardboard Box Fun Felt markers or ordinary crayons will help you turn cardboard cartons into toy stoves, refrigerators, cupboards, play houses, cars, trains, wagons, zoo cages and lots more besides. Turn a box upside down. Put holes in it just large enough to hold clothes pegs. Put numbers on the clothes pegs. Now all you need are some rubber jar rings for an easy ring-toss game.

Cut a large hole in the bottom of a cardboard box and make a clown's face around it. Make some bean bags and you've got a bean bag game. If white beans are expensive, try filling bean bags with popping corn.

Nut Shells The empty half shell of a peanut needs only a few dabs with a felt pen to make it into a finger puppet. Glue bits of felt to a half walnut shell and make a mouse. If you place a marble under the shell and put it on a sloped book, the mouse will scurry down! (But remember not to let small children play with marbles, lest they put them in their mouths.) Turn a half walnut shell the other way, put a paper sail on a toothpick and glue it on the shell. You have a sailboat. Make a fleet and have a bathtub regatta!

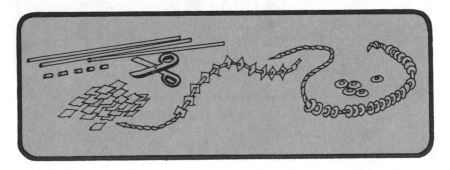

Wool and Such Bits String pieces of drinking straws and squares of coloured paper on strands of wool. If you wind a tiny piece of tape on the end of the wool, so that it is hard and pointed, it will be easier to use. Make another necklace by stringing the kind of cereal with holes in it. Make a sewing card by punching holes around an outline that you have drawn on cardboard. Look back at the 'INBETWEEN' on knots and hitches. The chain knot is fun for quite small children to learn on a long piece of wool. They think they're knitting! Really, they're crocheting because the chain knot is SC, or single crochet, in crochet work.

Paper Bags Make paper bag puppets. If you have an old broom handle, make it into a hobby horse with a paper bag horse's head. Decorate paper bags to make hats and all sorts of masks.

Make Modelling Play Dough The simplest modelling clay recipe consists of 2 cups of flour, 1 cup of salt and enough water to make a firm, but soft, dough. For coloured play dough, knead in some food colouring. Store it in a cool, dry place in plastic bags.

Finger Plays Do you remember some from your childhood? Here's one to start you remembering:

> *"Here is a bunny with ears so funny,*
> *And here is his hole in the ground.*
> *At each sound that he hears,*
> *He pricks up his ears,*
> *And hops to his hole in the ground."*

Dramatize nursery rhymes, using your whole self, or in finger-play fashion.

Action songs are fun. Most children love songs and enjoy imitating the actions. And do you know that lullabies really work? Gentle singing at bedtime can lull a child to sleep. Of course, you may sing so beautifully that the child won't want you to leave, but that's a good chance to take!

HOW MUCH DO YOU KNOW ABOUT CHILD CARE?

Read each statement below carefully. If you think it is true put a checkmark in the 'true' column. If you think it is false, check the 'false' column. The answers are on the next page.

What do you think?	True	False
1. More children are harmed by accidents than by any other cause.		
2. When you are baby-sitting, it is all right to watch a TV show, even if the child doesn't want to watch it.		
3. Cleaning materials, e.g. furniture polish, should be kept under the sink.		
4. If a child doesn't want to do something, or cries for her mother, you should try cheering her up by having some candy on hand to give her.		
5. Only minor injuries, such as small cuts should be treated by you if you're baby-sitting. Otherwise, an adult's advice should be asked.		

What do you think?	True	False
6. If you are baby-sitting, you should have a list of emergency phone numbers: child's doctor, fire department and police.		
7. If you are baby-sitting and the child is asleep, it is a good idea to ask a girlfriend over to keep you company.		
8. Insist that the parents leave written instructions of how to contact them if you are looking after their child in their absence.		
9. Children should be encouraged to help dress and feed themselves.		
10. If you are baby-sitting and get hungry, look around for something to eat.		
11. It is wise to know where the exits in the house are when you are baby-sitting.		
12. Children usually prefer small helpings at meals.		
13. If a child says "my mother lets me do it", he's sure to be right and you should let him do whatever it is.		
14. Young children need to be cuddled.		
15. If a child has a bowel movement in his diaper or pants, you should leave the soiled pants in the washbasin for the mother to look after when she comes home.		
16. If a child falls on his head, and soon afterwards gets sleepy or vomits, a doctor should be called.		

What do you think?	True	False
17. Once a child is three years old, it is alright to leave him alone in the bathtub while you go and do something else.		
18. If someone comes to the door and says he is a friend of the family for whom you are baby-sitting, ask him in.		
19. It's a good idea to have a lively 'roughhouse' session with children just before bedtime to wear them out.		
20. The most important things in child care are keeping the child safe, healthy and happy.		

The answers, and brief explanations, follow. It is a good idea to discuss them with your mother or someone else who is knowledgeable about child care.

1. True.   Accidents in the home cause most child injuries and deaths.

2. False.   If you are absorbed in a TV programme, you won't likely pay much attention to the child in your care.

3. False.   These are poisons and should be kept well out of child's reach, preferably in a locked cupboards.

4. False.   Bribing a child with candy is asking for trouble. She will always expect it. Moreover, it's bad for her teeth and general health.

5. True.   If you have any doubt about an injury, seek adult advice.

6. True.   Keep these close to the telephone. Know the telephone number and name of a neighbour who would help in an emergency.

7. False. Baby-sitting is a job. The parents have hired you, not your friend as well.

8. True.   This is absolutely necessary for your sake and their sake. Insist on it!

9. True.   Children enjoy taking on responsibilities with assistance.

10. False. It's nice if they leave you something to eat, but don't be nosy.

11. True.   This is good to know wherever you are in case of fire.

12. True.   Small, even very small, helpings encourage children to eat.

13. False. Children often say something like this just to get their own way. Use your common sense. If in doubt, remember what your mother let you do at that age.

14. True.   A child needs to be shown he's loved.

15. False. Swish the diaper in the toilet to remove all the excreta, then flush it away (but hold on to the diaper!). Rinse the diaper out in hot water and put it in a diaper pail or plastic bag. Follow package directions for disposable diapers.

16. True.   Sleepiness and vomiting after a fall are signs of serious head injury.

17. False. Never leave a child alone in a bathtub. He can drown in an inch of water.

18. False. Never let anyone in unless you know the person well and have been given permission. Keep the doors locked and don't open them for strangers.

19. False. A quiet story is much better. Too much activity simply excites the child.
20. TRUE! IF YOU CAN DO THESE THREE THINGS YOU ARE A GOOD BABY-SITTER.

ECOLOGY AND YOU

Ecology is the study of the interrelationships among all living and life-giving things. Sometimes, because people invent such awesome machines as the computer, or rocket ships that will reach out into space, we forget about these relationships. Just think for a moment. What would happen if all the earth's waters dried up? We would die. Suppose grasshoppers lost all their natural enemies and multiplied a million times? They would eat all our grains. Suppose . . . well, you think of what might happen if . . .

Animals, birds, people, insects live and continue to breed only as long as their kind of food is available. How many food chains can you think of? People eat beef from cattle which eat grass which grows in good soil, thanks to the sun and the rain and rotting vegetation to fertilize it. Owls eat mice which eat grubs which feed on acorns which grow on oak trees which grow in good soil. What happens if you remove one part of a food chain? It breaks down. And it can spell disaster. For example, if you were to kill all the dragonflies around a pond, you find many, many more mosquitoes because mosquito larvae are a favourite food of dragonflies.

When we interfere with the natural environment, we often upset its very delicate balance. Natural 'garbage', like dead leaves and unwanted food, rots and gradually returns to soil. Unnatural garbage, like metals, plastics and glass don't rot. They remain unchanged for centuries. Do you know what happens to the garbage in your community? Find out! How much garbage does your family have in a week? Can you think of ways to make it less? What would you do if there were no garbage collection for six months?

Some activities to try

— When you go shopping, count how many items have unnecessary packaging. Plastics are made from oil, and some day the world's supply will run out. Paper is usually made of wood pulp, and although you can plant more trees, they take a long time to grow to maturity. Some people send unnecessary packages back to the manufacturer along with a letter to say why.

— Write down ten electrical appliances used in your home. Put an X beside any that weren't available in your parents' childhood (ask them). Put a line through any you think you could live without. Write down beside each one what you could substitute, if there were no electrical power available.

— Find out what plants and shrubs attract different birds because their flowers, fruit or seeds provide food. Plant some and see if new birds come to your garden.

— Find out if there are any naturalist organizations you could join. They may have magazines with lots of interesting ideas.

— Does your camp have any nature trails. They are fun to set up. Make permanent information markers that can be firmly attached (perhaps to posts) without damaging trees. Try a 'sense trail'. For example, a marker identifying a beech tree might suggest touching the bark to feel its smoothness; a marker identifying wintergreen might suggest tasting it; a marker identifying skunk cabbage would ask you to follow your nose to find the plant!

— Does your camp have a problem with flies near its latrines?

Find out what kind of plants repel flies, for example, yarrow and tansy, and plant them around the lats.

— Make a pollution jar. Put water in a jar, then put in various kinds of garbage, like aluminum foil, dirty paper scraps, apple peel, dirt, and so forth. Leave it for a month, then see what it looks like. Is your nearest river like that?

— Make a habit of recycling as much as you can. Using something once and throwing it away makes little sense if it could be reused or remade into something else.

"My husband said I was crazy to let a bunch of Guides talk me into going out at dawn to cook breakfast because they claimed they could think better while eating. He was right!" Mrs. Weston looked despairingly at Mrs. Mac. "We haven't even started to discuss anything seriously, and we'll soon have to pack up and head for home. If I remember correctly, the reason for this outrageously early hour was because Lynn and Helen have to play in a basketball tournament at 10:30."

Mrs. Mac looked at the group of Patrol Leaders and Seconds. The remains of a potluck gourmet breakfast, with such delicacies as French toast and strawberry crêpes, lay on a ground sheet. Sprawled on ground sheets nearby were the girls, looking very full and lazy.

"I feel just like they look," said Mrs. Mac. "I guess I'd better remind them why we're here." She tried to look businesslike. "Everyone had enough to eat?" A chorus of satisfied murmurs answered her. "I believe we had a motion at the last Court of Honour that we hold this one at a cook-out, because you all found it easier to think after a meal cooked outside. So I presume you're now all full of bright ideas, and that Pam has the minute book and her pen somewhere in that knapsack of hers."

"It's here somewhere." Pam dug frantically in the pockets of her knapsack. "I've got it . . . oh-h . . . it's a bit sticky. The syrup bottle leaked."

"Lick it off," came a voice.

"Use my wet towel," said another.

Pam read the minutes, and grinned at Lynn when she came to the last sentence. "It was moved by Lynn, seconded by Helen, that we have a special Court of Honour to discuss the requirements for those who want to be Patrol Leaders and to settle the details about Patrol Leader elections. The motion carried. It was moved by Helen and seconded by Lynn that this meeting be at a breakfast cook-out at Greenside Park. Motion carried."

It soon became apparent that there was a lot of disagreement over who should be allowed to run for Patrol Leader.

"When I told the kids in my patrol that we needed four new Patrol Leaders, because two of us are going to Rangers and one to Cadets, and Helen's too involved in sports to continue as P.L., they all said they thought anyone who wanted to run should be allowed to, even if they'd just been enrolled."

"We had a hassle at our Patrol in Council," said Helen. "Everyone thought you should have some badges to be able to run as P.L., but we couldn't agree on how many — or which ones. Lisa said two indoor and two outdoor badges, and then we argued over which badges were indoor and which were outdoor. Finally, I got them to let me say that whoever runs should have *some* badges."

"Why did they think it was important to have badges?" asked Mrs. Mac.

"I'm not sure. Partly because the one who most wants to be P.L. has a lot of badges, but I don't think she's the best one for the job. She's bossy. Anyhow, having a lot of badges doesn't mean you get along with other kids. She's a ... I shouldn't say it, I guess, but you all know who I mean and... " Helen looked uncomfortable as she finished " ... she wouldn't help somebody else if it didn't help her, too."

"We talked about that, too," said Lynn. "You know how organized Chris is. She had it all figured out. We discussed why we liked some kind of Patrol Leaders and not others — stuff like being good at camping and hiking, being able to lead games and songs and talk in front of everybody, being fun and kind and helping other kids learn new things. Chris had made a list of badges that sort of fitted in with what we thought a P.L. should be like and ..."

"You mean there's a badge for being fun?" interrupted Helen. "Lead me to it!"

"Not exactly," said Lynn. "Chris couldn't put everything in, but she tried. Anyhow, we didn't agree on it, because we realized that the list would mean some people could never run for P.L."

"How do you mean?"

"We realized it when we came to the part about speaking in front of everybody. And we thought of Terry in your patrol, Jan. She's so shy when there's a lot of people around. She has a speech impediment and I guess that makes her even more shy, and she blushes so easily. But when there are only a few kids, she's just super. And most of the time a P.L. has only a few kids — just her own patrol. If you have to run a game or something, you can get somebody else to do it for you."

Jan, who hadn't spoken yet, looked pleased. "Terry is the kindest kid I've ever known. She doesn't put it on either. Maybe it's because she doesn't talk all the time. She seems to know when somebody needs something, and if someone's unhappy, she knows how to cheer her up."

"What did your patrol decide, Jan?" asked Mrs. Weston.

"Well, gee, we didn't have any problems deciding. We just thought that if someone wanted to run for P.L., they should be allowed to. It doesn't mean they'll be elected. We do think there should be more than four running, so that we have to make a choice."

"That's about what our patrol thought, too," said Melanie. "We went through the badge thing and Maria..." she looked at her Second "... you tell them, Maria."

"I said 'how about me?' and they looked at my badge scarf with its two lonely badges."

"You've started lots of badges," said Mrs. Mac. "Too bad we couldn't put all the bits and pieces together!"

"I'm not all that interested in getting badges, but I like doing stuff that you do when you work on badges. I'm just not much at finishing, that's all. But I still want to run for Patrol Leader, and the others thought Guides like me should have a chance."

Melanie continued, "So we ended up thinking that anyone who wants to run should be able to. We also thought of having campaign speeches, like they do in government elections, but I guess that's not such a good idea. We hadn't thought about Terry and maybe there are others like her."

"Can I make a motion, Mrs. Mac?" asked Helen. "I move that any Guide who wants to run for Patrol Leader should be allowed to."

"I second it," said Jan. "D'you think we should say something about them having to know what a Patrol Leader is supposed to do?"

"Everyone knows that," said Lynn. "At least, my patrol does. If yours doesn't, they should see our list. It's got things on it that I could never be like. And I've been Daffodil Patrol Leader for a long time."

Everyone laughed. "How did looking at the list make you feel, Lynn?" asked Mrs. Mac.

"When Chris first showed us — she'd made up a list at home of her idea of a good P.L. — I said it sure didn't describe me!"

"Did you feel the list was criticizing you?" asked Mrs. Weston.

"Me?" said Lynn in surprise. "No way! I mean, it was too perfect. Like nobody's that perfect! Especially me. Anyhow, when they elected me P.L., they knew what they were getting."

"I think it's a good idea to know what a Patrol Leader is supposed to do, before you say you'll run," said Jan. "When I told my mum I had to be in charge of things and phone kids and all that, she almost wouldn't let me be P.L., in case I didn't get my practising done and in case I tied up the telephone. She gets mad if I'm on the phone too much, because she's in real estate, and once she missed a big sale when my brother was talking to his girl friend."

"O.K.," said Helen. "Can I change my motion and say 'anybody who understands the duties of a Patrol Leader and wants to run'? Is that better?"

Everyone looked happy with that. Mrs. Mac said, "We really should have an amendment to the first motion Helen made, but that gets complicated. If Pam has the change written down," (Pam nodded) "I think we're ready for the vote. Will you read the motion, Pam?" Pam read the motion and it carried unanimously.

"Now, when and how will we have the election?" asked Mrs. Mac.

That was an easy question to decide. Two weeks would give girls lots of time to decide if they wanted to run for Patrol Leader. The P.Ls decided to make out ballots, much the same as those used in government elections, with the names of the candidates in alphabetical order. Everyone would be asked to put a check mark or an 'X' beside their four choices. They would set up cardboard screens so that everyone could mark their ballots secretly.

"And next week, we can get everyone to write down on slips of paper who they want to be with in a patrol — if it matters to them — because electing four new Patrol Leaders will mean changes anyhow," said Lynn. "If four Daffodils get elected, and I've gone to Rangers, there'll only be one Daffodil left!"

On election night, Jenny and Carol walked home together from Guides.

"Well, it happened, Jenny," said Carol. "We both got elected Patrol Leaders. We've been Daffodils together for so long, it's going to be funny to be in different patrols. Who're you going to choose as your Second?"

"Chris, I think. She's next door, and that's handy, and she's good at things I'm not good at, like organizing. I get confused. Who will you choose?"

"I think I'll ask Lori. She's always so afraid she can't do something right. Maybe being Second would help her. She can do things a lot better than she ever thinks she can. I'll have to get used to being a Robin!"

"Yeah," said Jenny. "I was glad I won the toss to see which of us would stay with the Daffodils. Did you mind?"

"Not really. I kinda hoped it would be me who could stay a Daffodil, but getting to be a Robin P.L. means I start out with a nice tidy patrol box. Not like the Daffodil one!"

"Jenny, have you noticed anything different about Lori lately?" Carol suddenly asked her friend.

"What d'you mean? How?"

"Sometimes when she comes to Guides, she looks as if she's been crying and she's often late. She never used to be late," said Carol. "I asked her once if there was something the matter, and she just said 'no' and turned away.

"I felt funny about it — the look on her face, I guess — and I wondered if I'd done something. But she's always liked me, I thought."

"Maybe you'll find out when you ask her to be your Second. I'm glad we choose our own Second. I wouldn't like to have someone I didn't get along with very well."

"I'd better go in now," said Carol. "My mum starts worrying if

I'm late. She never remembers how fast time goes when you're talking — or at least, when *I'm* talking. I want to phone Lori and see if she'll come over after school tomorrow. I've got the Robin Patrol log book with me and I want to get Lori to put the new names in it and make some drawings on the page. She's so good at doing that."

The next day, when Lori was sitting at Carol's kitchen table working on the log book, Carol asked her to be her Second. To Carol's amazement, Lori burst into tears and cried with great, choking sobs.

"Lori, what's the matter? What did I say wrong? I just want you to be my Second. Lori, tell me what's wrong." Carol was completely bewildered.

"I c-can't, Carol. I can't," said Lori, between sobs.

"Can't what? Can't be my Second?" asked Carol. "Oh Lori, that's not true. You'd be a good Second, and I really want you more than anyone else. Here, have a tissue."

She sat waiting while Lori blew her nose and wiped her eyes. "I'm sorry, Carol. That's not it at all. I want to be your Second. But everything's gone wrong." She started to cry again. She looked so small and hunched over that Carol wanted to hug her and comfort her. "If it was me crying like that, I'd want someone to hug me," she thought. She got up, and putting her arms around Lori, held her tightly. She thought Lori would never stop crying. Finally, her sobs grew less and she managed a weak smile through her tears.

"I think I'll be O.K. now, Carol. I'm glad your brother's not home."

"He wouldn't think anything of it," said Carol. "He says girls cry all the time, which isn't true; but sometimes you just have to cry, and there's nothing wrong with that."

Lori didn't say anything for a minute, then suddenly, very loudly and abruptly, she said, "My mother and father are getting divorced." Tears filmed her eyes again, but she brushed them back.

"Oh Lori," said Carol. She didn't know what else to say.

"Can I tell you about it? I haven't told anyone. It's hard to say out loud."

"Sure, Lori."

"I guess I've really known for a long time, but I pretended and pretended it wasn't happening. My mother and father haven't gotten along together for... almost since I can remember. They've had fights, not the kind where you hit each other, but terrible arguments. I could hear them after they thought I was asleep. Twice my mother and I went and lived somewhere else. And once, she just left and stayed away a whole month."

"What did you do then, without her, I mean?"

"At first, my dad and I were alone and then he found a housekeeper. She was nice but I just hated her. Anyhow, my mother came back and everything was pretty good for quite a long time. But then they started fighting again, worse than ever, and it's just..." Lori started to cry again.

"Don't they like each other?" asked Carol. It sounded like something on a television show. "My mum and dad argue sometimes, but I never thought it meant they didn't like each other... they root for different hockey teams and they never vote the same way in an election."

"That's not what my mother and father argue about. It's... well, it's just different. I don't know if they've ever liked each other really. My dad swears at my mum and she throws things, not at him, but just throws things. If I did what they do, they'd get mad at me, but when they do it to each other, they don't care."

"My Uncle Gerry's divorced," said Carol. "I don't remember his first wife, but my cousin Jody lives with him and his new wife. She's nice and Jody likes her."

"I'm not ever going to live with my dad," said Lori bitterly, "and I don't want him to marry anybody else. I don't think it's fair.

He's going to stay here and move into an apartment. My mother says she'll have to go back to work full time and she's going to take me to my grandmother's. It's not even in this province and it's out in the country, and my mother will have to drive into the city every day because she's going to work for a newspaper where she worked before she was married. I'll have to go to school on a bus. That'll be fun, but I won't know anyone."

"Won't you ever see your father?" asked Carol.

"Once or twice a year, maybe. There's something called custody. That's when they decide whether your mother or your father gets you."

"Who decides it? Don't you get to decide?"

"The court decides it. They asked me who I wanted to stay with, but how could I decide something like that?" answered Lori. "Even if they don't love each other, I still love both of them. But if I stayed with my dad, he'd have to get a housekeeper and I wouldn't like that. I want my mum. He's out of town one week every month on business and I'd be a problem. Anyhow it seemed easier to say I'd go with my mother to my grandmother's place. I like my grandmother a lot, even if I don't see her often.

"It's been so awful at our house for so long. My mother says my dad won't let her have a thought of her own or do anything she wants to do, and she says he wastes too much money on new cars and stuff. Maybe they'll be happier when they're a thousand kilometres apart."

"Maybe it'll be better for you too, Lori," said Carol. "At least, you won't have to listen to them fight. Won't that be better?" Carol wished there was something she could say to help.

"I know," replied Lori. "But I wish they could stay together and not fight. They say they've tried that too many times and it doesn't work. I hate God! Why can't He make them not fight?"

Carol suddenly knew the depth of Lori's feelings. It was the loss of all she held dear — her family, her home, her friends, Guides, school. Carol had once felt something like that, too.

"When I was eight," said Carol, "my dog was run over and I'd had him ever since I was a baby. It took him two days to die and I thought nothing would ever be the same again. I yelled at God for letting him die. My mother said it was better for him to die than to suffer, but that wasn't what I wanted either. I wanted him not to have been run over in the first place, just like you want your mum and dad not to be the kind that fight with each other.

"I was unhappy about my dog (his name was Prince) for a long, long time. I even hated other kids who had dogs."

"How did you stop feeling unhappy?" asked Lori. There was a ray of hope in her voice.

"Well, I guess it was partly that I got older (I even hate saying this because it sounds disloyal to Prince and I really loved him), but I forgot about him lots of times, unless something happened to remind me. I loved him, but I was doing different things, so I didn't miss him as I did when he first died. Most people have some kind of trouble. Just different ones, that's all. My dad told me it was part of being a human being. He said it was what you did with your troubles that mattered. And when I blamed God, he said that wasn't very sensible, because if we could blame God for every-thing, we'd never be responsible for anything ourselves."

"But losing a dog isn't like losing your family," said Lori. "You can get another dog."

"But I didn't want *another* dog," answered Carol. "I wanted Prince. He'd been my best buddy all my life, and losing him was the worst thing that ever happened to me."

"I'm sorry," said Lori, "I didn't mean what I said. At least I'll be living with my mum and I can see my dad. D'you know that when I come to see him I get to travel in an airplane? I don't want to talk about it anymore. But that's why I can't be your Second."

"Gee, I'd almost forgotten about that! Listen, when will you be moving?"

"When everything legal's settled. A couple of months, probably."

"Well then, be my Second until you move. Will you?"

"O.K.," said Lori, and for the first time that afternoon, she smiled. "I'll keep the log book fixed up so that it's really nice, too. Will you tell Mrs. Mac for me? I'd like to talk to her about it, but every time I start talking about it, I cry. I'd rather she knew first and then maybe I won't cry so much when I talk to her. My nose always runs so much when I cry!"

It was Lori's last night at Guides. The company was having a farewell pyjama party in the church hall for her. Each patrol had agreed to be responsible for one hour's activities. At first, they wanted them to be a total surprise, but when Jenny had wondered what would happen if every patrol decided to bring records and dance for an hour, or to bring food and eat for an hour, they realized a bit of organization was needed.

Jenny's patrol was in charge of a craft hour. After long discussions and looking through books and magazines, they hadn't come to any decision until one day after school, Chris had a bright idea.

Jenny, I've got it! What we can do at the party for Lori! I've been sitting here looking at your T-shirt and it gave me an idea. Why don't we ask everyone to bring an old, plain T-shirt and I'll ask my mum to lend us her liquid embroidery set and maybe somebody else has one too. Then we can draw things on the

T-shirts and sign our names — like walking autograph books!"

The rest of the Daffodils were enthusiastic over Chris's idea. They asked everyone to bring a T-shirt and to be prepared for it to look different when they took it home.

The Robins were in charge of the campfire and asked all the patrols to contribute a 'remember when' skit. Carol explained, "The skit has to start out with the words 'remember when we...' and then you have to act out, without words, something we've done, especially something funny, so that Lori will remember us. We all have to guess what it is you're remembering. And it can't take longer than three or four minutes."

Near the end of the campfire, Carol presented Lori with a set of acrylic paints as a farewell gift from the company.

"We hope you'll enjoy using them, Lori, and maybe you'll send us a picture of your new school or something, and we'll put it on the bulletin board. Now, Mrs. Mac has something she want to say."

"Thanks, Carol. Lori, I've found out that you can still be a Guide if you want to. I told the Commissioner that you're going to be a long way from any town where they have Guides. She said she'd find out about Lones in the province you're moving to. Most provinces have Lone Brownies and Guides and Rangers for girls who live too far away from an active group.

"Lones don't have weekly meetings like we do. They have a

Guider who keeps in touch with them by mail and sometimes by telephone or tapes. She sends them letters suggesting things to do and learn about. They have handbooks and work on badges and any other activity that interests them, by themselves or with a friend. The letters go to each girl and sometimes from one girl to another so that the girls can add messages, and get to know each other that way. Sometimes they all meet together for a special event, or join in with an active company. Sometimes they have Lone camps just for them, or they go camping with other Guides. Would you like that, Lori?"

"Wow!" said Lori. "Would I ever!"

"Could we send her letters, too, Mrs. Mac?" asked Pam. "Like we do with the company in Australia. Maybe we could send tapes as well! Have you got a tape-recorder, Lori?"

"No," replied Lori. "But I've been saving my money for a long time to buy a record player. Maybe a tape-recorder would be a better idea."

"We could even record a whole Guide meeting for you," suggested Carol, excitedly.

Mrs. Mac looked doubtful. "Well, you could try, I suppose. But it might sound like a herd of elephants! Try recording people getting up from the floors or chairs. It sounds like a factory!"

"Anyhow," said Lori. "You could sing new songs you learn, and I could sing them along with you when I get the tape. Or you could tell me jokes. I might even hear a whole bunch of new jokes that you guys haven't heard, and I could tell them to you."

"Sounds good," said Mrs. Mac. "I think you'll enjoy being a Lone Guide, Lori. It means you'll have to do a lot on your own, but maybe you'll find a new friend who'd like to be a Lone Guide with you. And if you're back here staying with your father this summer when we go to camp, you know we'd love to have you camp with us."

At the last Guide meeting in June, Carol brought a letter she had just received from Lori. Mrs. Mac suggested she read it to everyone at campfire.

"Dear Carol,

This is going to be a lot different from my other two letters to you! For one thing it won't be all soggy from tears. I'll tell you the most important things first. Or first and second, because they go together.

The man who rents my grandmother's land to grow crops on, came round last week with his son. He's just finishing grade eight and his name's Eric. He has red hair and he'll probably be good-looking because his father is. (You can't tell yet, but *I* think he's good-looking.) Anyway, that doesn't matter because he owns, *all by himself*, two horses and he's teaching me how to ride!!! If my grandmother lets him, he

says we can keep one of the horses here. It's a mare. She's gentle and her name's Tessie, which is a dumb name for a horse, but she's brown and I just love her. It's really, really great learning how to ride and Eric never makes fun of me or anything like that. Those are the two most important things. In case you're wondering which is most important, I dream a lot about Tessie. Fooled you, didn't I?

Another important thing is that I'm a Lone Guide. There are seven of us in the Lone Company and every month we get a newsletter. It's not about news — just sometimes. It's mostly ideas for things to do and think about. When we're working on a badge we get ideas for that, too, if we need them. I've finished the Baker Badge that I started two years ago. My grandmother showed me how to make pie and that was the only thing I had left to do. Now I'm ready to be tested for the Astronomer Badge. We have a neighbour on the next farm who's a member of the Royal Astronomical Society of Canada. He has a neat telescope that he made himself. The sky here is fantastic. You can see more of it because we don't have tall buildings. When I get that badge I will have my Woodlore Emblem finished too.

Our Lone Guide Company has been invited to a neat-sounding camp down south. Because there's only a dammed-up creek for swimming, they don't have any boats like where we camped. But you know about me and water so I don't mind. I'm still scared of deep water! This camp's going to be called 'Future Ahead', and we're going to do a whole lot of stuff that's space-ageish, if you know what I mean. I'm not sure how it's going to work exactly, but they told us some interesting ideas they have for it and asked us for any thoughts we have. I sent in some. I've been reading a lot of science fiction books and they gave me some ideas. I made up a Martian wide game, and if you like, I'll send you the directions!

Another thing that's happened is that the school I go to has turned out better than I thought it would at first. They've got Lunch Hour Clubs because most of us come by bus, and I've joined three — the Sketch Club which I like best, and the Gymnastic Club and the POE Club. That stands for Preserve Our Environment and Eric's the president of it.

The other really good news I've saved for the last. My dad said I can come camping with you this summer, too! I'm going to stay with him for August, but the camp week is the only week he isn't on holiday. He's going to give my camp fee to Mrs. Mac and I'm putting the forms you sent me in with this letter. My mother signed them. She says she'll miss me but she doesn't get any holidays this summer.

Say Hello to everyone and if you want, you can let the other kids read this. See you in August!

Love from your old friend and Second,

LORI

P.S. If the envelope is wet it's because I let Tessie lick it.
P.P.S. If you want to know what the Martian game is like, tell me.
P.P.P.S. Write soon!!!"

INBETWEEN 7

**WHAT KIND OF PATROL LEADER
WOULD YOU LIKE TO BE?**

This is a list, drawn up by Guides, of the qualities of a good Patrol
Leader. Can you rank them first, second, third, etc., in the order
that *you* think is most important?

kind _____   sense of humour _____

clever _____   not bossy _____

tidy_____   popular _____

reliable _____   listens to others _____

fair _____   enthusiastic_____

good at organizing_____   full of good ideas_____

trustworthy_____   polite _____

cheerful _____   punctual_____

Now — you make a list of the kind of
patrol *member* you'd like to be!

_____

_____

_____

_____

_____

Try an acrostic. Write down the name of your patrol vertically and
fill in words beginning with each letter to describe your patrol.
Here's an example using 'Robin'.

R - ambunctious
O - bedient (and rambunctious?)
B - usy
I - maginative
N - oisy (sounds right!)

So you've been elected a patrol leader! Here are some duties you
might have

(i) Be responsible for
     patrol corner

(ii) Be responsible for
     patrol box and
     equipment

(iii) Help patrol members
      learn

(iv) Keep patrol members
     informed

(v) Lead patrol in games

(vi) Lead patrol in duties such as opening ceremonies, campfire planning, clean-up, etc.

(vii) Take patrol attendance

(viii) Collect dues and balance the dues book

(ix) Represent patrol at Court of Honour meetings

(x) Find out what patrol members are interested in doing

(xi) Wear uniform properly and encourage patrol members to do same

(xii) Help new members to feel comfortable in patrol

(xiii) Be a good listener to patrol members

(xiv) Help strengthen the patrol as a group

But you don't have to do it alone!

The best kind of leaders share their responsibilities with others. Think of ways that you can share the above tasks with members of your patrol. You are responsible for seeing that they are done. That doesn't mean you have to do them all yourself, or all by yourself. Help others develop their leadership abilities, too. Above all, share with your Second. She needs to feel wanted also. Don't be the cause of your Second saying, as more than one has, "I wish my Patrol Leader would get sick; then I'd have something to do."

THINGS TO REMEMBER WHEN
YOU'RE IN CHARGE OF A GAME

Nothing is more fun than a good game. Playing games teaches you much — good sportsmanship, patience, confidence, increased physical skills, mental alertness, co-ordination — ever so many things, depending on the kind of game. But above all, a game is fun.

1. Choose the game to suit your purpose. Are the Guides full of energy? Choose a running-around kind of game. Do you want to practise your observation skills? Choose a game that involves exercising your powers of observation. There are lots of game books available, either from the Guide Distribution Centre or your public library.

2. Know the rules of the game thoroughly, even if you have to practise saying them out loud to yourself.

3. Don't start explaining the game rules until everyone is listening. Hold your hand up for silence, and wait for it before speaking.

4. After you have given the instructions for a game, ask for questions to make sure everyone has understood.

5. If it seems necessary, have a 'dry run' of the game before actually playing.

6. If the game is to be scored, have someone else keep score on paper, or by using something like beans as counters.

7. Have someone else watch for first and second place if there are to be winners, as in a relay.

8. If the game doesn't seem to be working out as you thought it would, stop the game and quickly discuss why, changing the rules if necessary to suit your circumstances.

9. Elimination games, such as 'Musical Chairs,' should be used with care. People don't like standing around watching others play. Figure out a way to keep everyone playing, if possible.

10. Don't let people argue over a decision you've made, unless it's very obvious to you that you've made a mistake.

11. The best time to stop a game is when people want to keep on playing it. That way they'll enjoy it the next time. Don't play a game to death!

Games on file

Keep the directions for games you enjoy or games you'd like to try. Write them down on recipe file cards, or in a book, or on cardboard with felt pens.

Here are some sample games.

Try an active game — Topple Bottle

Equipment: Four empty plastic bottles, one or more bean bags, depending on number of players.

To Play: The players stand in as large a circle as possible. One person stands in the middle with the four bottles set up on the floor beside her, about 40 cm. from each other. The players in the circle attempt to knock down the bottles with the bean bags. The person in the centre stands them up as fast as she can. Whoever is successful in knocking down the last bottle, so that none remain standing, replaces the person in the centre.

Try a quiet game — Triple Threat

To Play: The players sit in a circle. One person starts the game by saying a name, a place and a food beginning with A, for example, "I am Angela from the Argentine and like applesauce." The next person does the same with B and so on through the alphabet. Note that you do not have to remember what the person before you said. If anyone can't think of something she is given a bean, rather than being eliminated. The object of the game is to end up with no beans.

Try an acting game — International Shopping

To Play: The players are in patrols, grouped in various parts of the room. The game leader has a list of items that could be bought in a store. One person from each patrol, the 'shopper', comes to the leader. All are given the same items. They return to their patrol which is the 'shop' and act out what they want to buy, because the 'shopkeepers' don't understand English. The first patrol to guess correctly wins, and new 'shoppers' go to the game leader. Try these items: umbrella, pound of butter, jar of honey, wedding ring, bikini, ballet shoes, pencil sharpener, bicycle pump, automobile tire, nosedrops.

Try an observation game — How much do you see?

This is one of the simplest, yet most difficult, observation games. Do you really notice your meeting place? Tell everyone you're having an observation game and send them outside to stand so many paces from the door for five minutes. While they are gone, write down a number of questions about the room they have just left — how many windows, position of fire extinguisher, pictures on the wall, flooring, etc. Go out to the players with papers and pencils and ask your questions. They will be surprised! Double their surprise by thinking up questions about the outside while they are writing the answers to your indoor questions. Ask those questions when you go back inside.

IDEAS CHOICES DECISIONS

A Guide company's activities are based on what the Guides want to do. The best place to find that out is by discussing ideas with your patrol. If you want to be formal, you call this a meeting of the Patrol in Council.

One way to gather a lot of ideas in a short time is to brainstorm. The P.L. asks everyone to think of all the things she'd like to do over the next few weeks. As fast as an idea comes to her, she says it aloud. Somebody, perhaps the P.L. but probably whoever can write the fastest, writes the ideas down. If she uses a china marker or felt pen and a large sheet of paper on the wall for everyone to see, it's more effective than if she just writes on a little piece of paper. After a lot of ideas have been put down, without discussing whether they are good or bad, possible or impossible, you start looking at them all. They are all CHOICES from which you choose what *you* want to do. Some ideas will interest only one or two, some will be enthusiastically adopted by the whole patrol.

The P.L. listens carefully to everyone's opinion. She makes notes (if she's smart she'll have a special notebook) of who wants to do what and what ideas are most popular. Her notebook might look like this:

Breakfast hike — everyone, not on the 20th
Crafts — everyone except Jody and Marianne
Tracker Badge — Jody, Anne and Susan
Campfire — we want to learn some new songs
Cyclist Badge — everyone except Susan
Singer Badge — Kim
Visit the water-filtration plant — everyone
Can't we have a different kind of opening?
The other patrols make too much noise —
can't we do something about it?
Learn some folk dances — everyone

THE COURT OF HONOUR

The Court of Honour is a meeting of the Patrol Leaders and the Seconds, usually, with the Guiders. If a joint meeting with Brownies or Rangers is under discussion, invite the Brownie Guiders, Ranger Guider or some Rangers. The Court of Honour meets as often as necessary, about once a month; at least once every two months.

The Patrol Leaders present their patrols' thoughts for discussion at the Court of Honour. If there are six patrols, there will be a lot of ideas for the Patrol Leaders to choose from. That's where planning becomes very important. The Court of Honour wants as many ideas used as possible so that there are few disappointments. It's a good idea to come to Court of Honour knowing what things are most important to the patrol members.

Often, several activities can be worked into one. For example, a hike is also an opportunity to work on a variety of outdoor badge requirements if you plan it that way. Guides who are working on similar activities — crafts, Toymaker, Seamstress, or other badges involving working with one's hands — can do it in the same part of the hall. Girls interested in Singer or Campfire Leader Badge can make it an opportunity to learn and teach new songs to the company.

The Court of Honour is a good place to suggest the names of grown-ups who might come for a week or two, to help a few girls learn a new skill.

The Court of Honour is also where you look back on activities you have completed and discuss what you thought of them. This is called evaluation. You talk about what went well and what didn't go so well. That helps you with future plans. If a hike was less than successful because everyone had trouble lighting fires, you'll probably ask for a session on fire lighting so that it doesn't happen again. If a craft session flopped because the girls who were supposed to bring certain materials forgot, you'll find ways of helping them remember.

When you join Rangers, you'll discover that the total Ranger programme is worked out this way. They call it ISPPE. That's not a mysterious word from a far-off country. It's an acrostic and stands for five English words:

INVESTIGATE
SELECT
PLAN
PARTICIPATE
EVALUATE

It's a good way for a patrol and the Court of Honour to work, too.

INVESTIGATE all the ideas your patrol can think of.
SELECT the ideas that appeal to you most.
PLAN ways to carry out the ideas in Court of Honour.

PARTICIPATE as individuals, buddies, patrols, other groupings, or as a whole company.

EVALUATE afterwards what you did,
then
you're
ready
to
begin
again!

YOU'RE A PATROL LEADER
AND YOU HAVE PROBLEMS?

Most of the problems you'll have will be 'people problems'. Problems about things, like a table that keeps collapsing or a lack of pencils, are fairly easily corrected. Problems with people take more time and trouble. But people are worth infinitely more than things, and don't ever forget that! Let's look at some common problems.

"Sally never pays any attention to what I tell her. She talks all the time I'm talking and no matter what I do, she won't be quiet."

"Molly is always bossing the other kids around. You'd think she was the Patrol Leader. Nobody likes her at all."

"Every time I turn my back, Janice is grabbing something that belongs to somebody else and running off with it because she likes being chased."

"Donna loses points for our patrol because she doesn't come half the time and when she does, she doesn't do anything."

Try these steps to solve your problem:

1. State the problem in more than one way.
2. Look for the causes of the problem.
3. Think of several different solutions for the problem.
4. Decide which solutions seem the best.
5. Try them.

Let's apply these problem-solving steps to one of the above problems.

Step 1 (Restating the problem) I'm telling everyone what to do and Sally just keeps talking to the girl beside her about her boy friend. Sally is more interested in boys than in hearing what I have to say.

Step 2 (Looking for the reasons) Sally likes boys. I don't like listening to Sally and she knows it. Sally likes talking. Sally doesn't like doing what I tell her.

Step 3 (Thinking of solutions)

(a) Let somebody else tell them what to do.
(b) Give Sally a little time to talk about boys.
(c) Ask Sally if she'll let us do whatever it is and then we'll all listen to her.
(d) Ask that Sally be moved to another patrol.
(e) Tell Sally privately what we're going to do and have her tell the others.
(f) Try to ignore Sally and sit with our backs to her.

Steps 4 and 5 (Deciding and trying the best) If we tried (d) or (f) it would be hurting Sally and running away from the problem. (a) doesn't help me. I'll try a combination of (b), (c) and (e). It may make her feel important and we may get done what we want to do. It's worth trying.

Now, you try applying the problem-solving steps to the other three problems.

Private! Patrol Corner

Does your patrol have its own special part of your meeting hall?
Do you have some way of letting others know it's your corner? Try
making one of these:
a patrol flag or pennant
   a patrol banner
      a patrol poster
         a patrol screen

Treasure Trove in a Patrol Box

A large wooden box with handles and a lock is ideal, but if this is
beyond your means, use a sturdy cardboard box. Put rope handles on it for easy carrying. Or look for an old picnic basket,
perhaps in a secondhand store. Or make a huge canvas or burlap
tote bag with zippered pockets.

What you keep in the box is up to your patrol, but if you are just
starting out, here are some sugguestions:
Guide Handbook   Guiding for You   Trefoil Round the World
song book   game book   reference books and pamphlets   book of
prayers   pencils   pens   crayons   ropes   paper   glue   scissors
pins   tape   chalk   tacks   felt pens   compass   local maps   (city,
road and topographic) equipment for games like bean bags, balls,
plastic bottles   plastic and paper bags   first aid kit.

Do you have a Patrol Log Book?

Appoint a Keeper of the Log who will write down special patrol
activities, ideas you have, and things you'd just like to remember.
If someone has a camera, why not chip in, buy film and pay for
processing, then keep a photographic record of your patrol? You
could even have a Patrol Photographer.

Patrol Funds

If you have special patrol money, apart from company dues, you'll need a patrol treasurer and she'll need something in which to keep the money and a book in which to keep track of income and expenditures.

HOW MUCH DO YOU KNOW
ABOUT THE WOMEN OF CANADA?

DO YOU KNOW that it took women a long time to win the right to vote in provincial and federal elections? Women were expected to 'keep house and keep quiet'. When was the right to vote won in your province?

Manitoba, Saskatchewan, Alberta	— 1916
British Columbia and Ontario	— 1917
Nova Scotia	— 1918
New Brunswick	— 1919
Prince Edward Island	— 1922
Newfoundland	— 1925
Quebec	— 1940

Women were allowed to vote in federal elections after 1918.

HAVE YOU READ ABOUT ANY OF THE EARLY 'SUF-FRAGETTES' — WOMEN WHO WORKED TO GET THE VOTE AND THE RIGHT TO SIT IN PARLIAMENT? Here are some famous names. Look in your library for stories about them:

Nellie McClung; Dr. Emily Howard Stowe who had to go to an American Medical School because no Canadian one would admit her on account of her sex; Emily Murphy — Edmonton's and Canada's first woman police magistrate; Judge Helen MacGill — Canada's first woman judge; Mme Thérèse Casgrain.

319

HAVE YOU READ ANY BOOKS BY CANADIAN WOMEN? Why don't you keep a list of those you have read? Have you read any books by Emily Carr, who was both a painter and a writer?

Do you know about any world-famous Canadian women athletes?

Nancy Greene, the skier? Marilyn Bell who swam across Lake Ontario when she was sixteen, then swam the English Channel and the Strait of Juan de Fuca?

What about pioneer women adventurers?

Agnes Deans Cameron of Victoria made a six-month trip to the Arctic in 1908 with her niece and wrote a book about it. Anna Jameson toured Upper Canada (now Ontario) in 1837 by cart and canoe, then wrote a book about it. She called it 'the wildest and most extraordinary tour you can imagine'.

CAN YOU MAKE A LIST OF PROFESSIONS AND OCCUPATIONS? THEN DISCOVER WOMEN, PAST AND PRESENT, IN THESE OCCUPATIONS? Here is a start:

sculptor, dancer, singer, educator, engineer, inventor, astronomer, physician, film maker... you take it from here.

The bus driver braked to a stop and swung around in his seat.

"Well, we're here. You'll be glad they ploughed out this lane for you. Look at those snowbanks! How'd you like to have to carry your load from the highway through snow *that* deep?"

The Guides looked back at the long, narrow laneway the bus had just driven along to the camp buildings. The snow was as high as the window sills on the main lodge and at one end, had drifted as high as the eaves of the roof. Except for evidence of the snowplough, there was no sign of people having been there. The snow that had fallen off and on since Monday, covered everything with its unbroken whiteness. The sun was setting fast in the west and the dark silence of the winter's night was beginning to enclose the camp.

The girls tumbled out of the bus. "Wow! Just look — isn't it super?"

"Let's unload the stuff," shouted Jenny. "I'm hungry already!"

The bus driver opened the luggage hatch at the side of the bus. "If you girls will just take what I hand you, and get out of the way with it, we can do this pretty fast. I don't care if it's yours or somebody else's. Just take it and get moving. I gotta get back to town for my supper."

Jenny and Nancy came to attention and giggled. "Yes, *sir!*" they said. "You're the boss!" He had been a lot of fun on the trip to the camp. He sang along with them, whistling or making up his own words, which reduced them to gales of laughter.

With all hands working swiftly to carry sleeping bags, suitcases, knapsacks, snowshoes, skis, toboggans and grocery cartons to the lodge, the bus was soon empty. The driver blew on his hands to warm them and said, "O.K. kids. I'll be back Sunday at one. That's if it doesn't come down a blizzard. In that case, you'll be here for the winter like the groundhog and have to tunnel yourselves out!"

"Aw, c'mon," said Carol, "you wouldn't do that to us. You wouldn't want us to miss a math test at school on Monday. Anyhow, thanks a lot!"

"Yeah, thanks!" shouted everyone. "Thanks a million. And happy Thinking Day tomorrow."

The company had spent most of one Guide meeting organizing patrol duties for the weekend winter camp. Mary Kate, the Cadet who had been working with their company since fall, had helped them. The Cadets and Rangers camped together every winter. Some of them had joined the Guides for the weekend.

The lodge was cold and uninviting. Mary Kate gave an ear piercing whistle that made everyone jump.

"I need whichever patrol's on wood and water for tonight," she announced. "We need heat to cook supper and heat to keep warm. Right?"

"Right!" replied Jenny. "The Daffodils are on wood and water. What do you want us to do? You said last week that there was lots of wood cut."

"The wood's in the storage shed and if we all go over and use these totes to bring back big piles, we'll have enough to last for a while." Mary Kate took some canvas tote bags off a hook near the door as the Daffodils gathered around her. "We'll also pick up some pails to fill with snow to melt for washing. The water we brought from town is mostly for drinking and cooking, and we don't want to waste it."

It wasn't long before the huge fireplace at one side of the lodge was giving off a good heat. The old wood stove in the kitchen had pots of chili heating on it. Mrs. Mac watched a Ranger and Carol measure hot chocolate. The rest of Carol's patrol was busily sorting and shelving the food supplies.

"We're really grateful you Rangers and Cadets were free this weekend," said Mrs. Mac. "When the Guides first started talking about a winter camp weekend, Mrs. Weston and I didn't want to dampen their enthusiasm, but we didn't feel at all competent, despite all our summer camping experience. I'm not much of a cold-weather person, I guess, and the idea never appealed to me."

"We're only sorry that all of us couldn't come," replied the

Ranger. "The kids who go to Southridge High are all involved in their school winter carnival. Wasn't Cathy Schmidt once one of your Guides? She's sure to win the ice sculpture contest. We went over to see her last night and she made a group of rabbits that's just superb! Anyhow, we three Rangers and the two Cadets are here, and we're glad to help."

"We're glad you could come, too," said Carol. "When it hit us that Thinking Day was on a Saturday this year, we thought we'd like to be the first Guides in Canada to greet it. The only way we could think to do that was to have a midnight meeting. That made us think of coming to camp. You should've seen Mrs. Mac's face at Court of Honour when we started talking about camping in February!"

"And I thought I was hiding my feelings!" said Mrs. Mac. "It was lucky that Mrs. Weston remembered you are experienced in winter camping. We just hoped you'd come to the rescue." She looked up at a Guide who had been standing in the doorway of the kitchen.

"The tables are all set," said the Guide. "And Mrs. Weston said to tell you that we've all got our stuff put away and figured out where we're going to sleep. She also said to tell you that the lat's the coldest place in camp and she's put up a sign in it about leaving the light on. I don't know what good that'll do, but she says it will be some heat anyhow."

The Ranger laughed. "I was at the District meeting when the Brownie leaders suggested putting the electric wiring out to the Brownies' lat for them at night and all you Guide leaders thought the Brownies were sissies! Wait'll I tell them!"

About six weeks earlier each patrol had chosen a continent to be 'their' continent for the Thinking Day celebrations. Since then, they had been working at Guide meetings and at special patrol meetings to prepare activities representative of their continents. The midnight snack would consist of international food and would be a preview of the grand international banquet they'd planned for Saturday evening. Mary Kate had co-ordinated the patrols' plans.

After the dinner dishes had been done, everyone gathered in a circle. "I'm your tour guide," said Mary Kate, "for an exciting trip around the world this weekend. We're starting here in North America. The Fireweed Patrol is going to take you across the border to the United States."

One of the Fireweeds, dressed in the style of the 20's, came out of the sleeping area, accompanied by another Guide, similarly dressed and carrying a pencil and notebook. She was hard put to keep up with the rapid strides of the first.

"Mrs. Low, Mrs. Low," she said. "Could we sit down for a minute so that I can finish my interview. I really won't keep you long."

'Mrs. Low' stopped suddenly and said, "I'm sorry. These Girl Scouts keep me busy, you know. Now what was that you said?" She held up her hand to her ear.

"I've heard a lot of stories about you and how you started Girl Scouts in the United States after being a Girl Guide leader when you lived in Scotland. Is it true that you get leaders because you're deaf, and don't hear when people say 'no' to you?"

"Nonsense!" boomed 'Mrs. Low'. "I may be hard of hearing, but women all over the United States *want* to be Girl Scout leaders. Now take yourself: you're a fine young woman. Why don't you start a Girl Scout Troop? We need some more troops right here in Georgia. Fine state. I was born right here in Savannah."

"It is a fine state, Mrs. Low," stammered the 'reporter', "but I couldn't possibly be a Girl Scout leader. I'm too busy being a reporter, and anyhow I'm no good with girls."

"Fine, fine! That's settled then. I'll send you the books and you can start next Tuesday at seven. The girls will be delighted," and 'Mrs. Low' stalked back to the kitchen, followed by a bewildered 'reporter' who kept muttering, "I did not say yes, I did not say yes."

The Fireweed Patrol Leader stood up. She had an armload of small sticks. "That was Juliette Low, usually called Daisy," she said amid the clapping and laughter. "She founded the Girl Scouts of the United States of America after meeting Lord Baden-Powell. Before she died in 1927, she was responsible for the first World Conference to be held outside of England, at Camp Edith Macy in New York State in 1926. The delegates who came from the different countries each put a stick in the big fireplace there and made a wish for Guiding. We want you to do the same. We're going to give you these sticks that we've partly peeled. Write on it the name of a country from your continent — it has to be a member of the World Association and the list's on the wall over there. Then at midnight when we go out for our Thinking Day greeting we want each continent to make a wish for Guiding."

"Does it have to be a serious wish?" asked someone.

"It doesn't matter. It can be fun or serious, but not stupid. We'll give out the sticks now and a box of markers. You can do it while we get ready for Mexico and the West Indies."

Five minutes later, all the Fireweeds appeared in gay Mexican or West Indian costumes — a mixture of serapes, long embroidered skirts, straw hats, white shirts and jeans.

Mary Kate shoved a straw hat on her head. "Buenas noches, good evening!" she said. "Welcome to Mexico! Meet the Hot Tamales, the liveliest dancing group you've ever seen." The Fireweeds removed their hats in a grand, sweeping gesture. "They're going to teach you a Mexican folk dance. It took them only six weeks to master it, and now they can teach it to the rest of you in six minutes. You're on, Tamales!" She put on a record and the Fireweeds demonstrated their dance.

It was considerably more than six minutes later when the whole company sank to the floor, exhausted after their efforts. One of the Fireweeds, in a white, open-necked shirt and jeans, picked up a small oil can. "This is my poor portable steel drum," she said. "Welcome to the islands of the Caribbean. They are the most beautiful islands in the world. Sun, sand, gorgeous flowers. We would like you tourists to get to know our people better. We don't have a lot of money like you do, and we don't like you trying to buy our natural resources like sugar and minerals as cheaply as you can, but we're happy people. We have a lot of happy songs with a calypso beat. Sing along with us — the words are up on the wall there — so smile, and sing before we leave North America!"

After the lively calypsos, Mary Kate cleared her throat. "I'm just about out of voice," she said, "after that dance and those songs! We're going to leave North America now. Thanks a lot, Fireweed Patrol. Carol and the rest of the Robin Patrol are going to take us on a tour of the continent of Africa."

As Carol started to talk, Jenny put some more wood on the fire. It blazed up quickly, sending shadows dancing across the members of the Robin Patrol who were sitting near the fireplace.

"When we chose Africa," said Carol, "we thought it would be easy since some of us had done school projects on it. But when we got together and everyone brought books from the library, we discovered that there was so much to find out that we didn't even know where to begin. Then once we did begin, it was hard knowing where to stop!" She paused. "This is what we're going to do. Each one of us is going to tell what she thinks is the most interesting thing that she found out. Then we're going on safari. Safari is a Swahili word that came from an Arabic word meaning 'journey' or 'exploration'. And we're going to explore some songs and games from different countries in Africa. Sarah's going to start, then the rest of us will follow. O.K. Sarah, go ahead."

Sarah was the youngest member of the Robins. "I was interested to find out that African music is more complicated than European music and most people don't know that. African music was brought to North America by the slaves and my great-great-great-great-something-grandfather was a slave so he probably helped. The calypsos we just sang began in Africa and so did jazz."

The next Robin held up some pictures. "What really interested me was reading about a famous woman anthropologist, Mary Leakey. She digs up fossils in Olduvai Gorge in Tanzania — that's in East Africa; show them where on the map, Carol. They've even found human bones that are thousands of years old. They just keep digging and digging and find new layers of fossils. These pictures will show you what they're like."

"I was reading about how hard it is for native children to get to school in a lot of African countries," said another Robin. "If you're white, it's just like here — you have to go to school and everyone does. But in some countries, there aren't many schools for black children or they cost more money than they have and they're not as good. I even read about kids having to walk twelve kilometres a day just to get to school. They really want to get an education, more than we do, I guess. It made me feel selfish. And they have Guides in almost every country and sometimes they help educate other kids. The Rangers even teach health care and stuff like that to adults."

The next Guide wore bangles and necklaces. "I've got an uncle who works in Cairo, Egypt. He's married to my mother's sister. She's an artist and she met him when he was here in Canada at university. He's an architect. Egypt has one of the world's oldest civilizations. This poster has photographs of some buildings he helped design that are based on early Egyptian art. My aunt makes jewellery and she made these bracelets and necklaces."

Carol was the last to speak. "Before Christmas, at our church we saw a film that had a lot in it about Africa, especially about the countries along the wide part of the continent." She pointed at the big map the patrol had made. "People in these countries hardly ever have enough food, for themselves or their animals. This means they are often starving; not just hungry but really starving! If they don't get enough rain, their crops won't grow. They get all kinds of horrible diseases from not having the right kind of food. Well, I found out that there are ways we can help, but not by sending food which we don't need. It does some good, but not all that much. What the people need most is money for wells, and irrigation systems to provide water for when the rains don't come, and for a better kind of seed and animals.

Our patrol all brought our pennies for the Canadian World Friendship Fund. But that doesn't go to prevent world hunger. It's for Guide things around the world and some of it's for disasters like floods and earthquakes. It needs all our pennies too, but we wanted to do something *extra,* just for world hunger. So we've made a special bank. It's just an old plastic bowl with a lid. We put a slot in the lid for coins. It's empty, just like a lot of kids' stomachs. We're going to keep it in our patrol box and put money in it. When it's about full, we'll send it to a fund that helps countries find ways to get enough food for everyone."

Mary Kate pointed to pictures glued around the border of the map of Africa made by the Robins. "When you get a chance to see this up close, you'll see pictures of kids suffering from malnutrition and from diseases we never have in Canada. There are also pictures of big cities and little villages, and some of Girl Guides in different parts of Africa. Carol, did you want the other patrols to contribute to your hunger bowl?"

Carol nodded, "Yes, we do. You don't have to; just if you want to."

"It's time to go on safari now," said Carol's Second. "It'll take about an hour, Mrs. Mac. Will that be enough time to get the snacks ready before midnight?"

Mrs. Mac looked at her watch. "Oh, I think so. It isn't going to take that long to get the food ready."

"O.K.," said Carol. "Here's what you do. We're all going to sing the 'Rhodesian Clapping Game' song first, and then each patrol will go to a different part of the room to do what we've got there."

"In that corner," said Sarah, pointing, "are pictures of animals that you find only in Africa, and jack-knives, and pieces of a special kind of carving rock. It's called meerschaum and it's mined in Turkey but we got it at a hobby shop. You can try doing rock carvings there like you find in different parts of Africa. And over there we have a contest. You know how lots of girls in Africa can carry heavy loads on their heads? Well, we've got bun baskets and oranges. You have to see how many you can carry a certain distance and there's a prize."

"I bet you get to eat all the squished oranges that fall," whispered Jenny to the girl beside her.

"Over there," continued another Robin, "we've got a game for two patrols to play against each other. It's called 'Mulambilwa'. That other corner has a game called 'Match My Feet'. In the kitchen there's a slide show about Kenya. We borrowed the slides from Cathy's neighbour who went there."

Carol said, "You'll spend about ten minutes at each thing and then move on to the next, in order, when we beat the drums. Each safari stop has a big number on the wall near it. You won't have time to finish the carving but you can take it with you to do some other time. We'll give the Patrol Leaders the number where they are to start."

Mrs. Mac and Mrs. Weston watched the patrols sort themselves out and begin the safari. "Aren't they terrific!" said Mrs. Mac. "All the work they've gone to! And they're so imaginative. When I was a kid I couldn't have done half that."

"You always say that," rejoined Mrs. Weston. "Every time the

Guides come up with something like this, you're surprised. They hardly ever let us — or each other — down. Remember that first year — the first cook-out we had when you were so sure they'd forget half the stuff they said they'd bring?"

"I sure do," laughed Mrs. Mac. "I had that box of extra food tucked away in my car trunk and my family ate wieners for the next week! Let's go see if we can attach ourselves to a patrol. It looks like such fun!"

At a quarter to twelve, a long table covered with plates of temptingly delicious snacks, representative of many parts of the world, was set ready near the kitchen. The girls were jostling each other in the lodge entranceway as they put on boots and ski jackets.

Barb Hunter, a Ranger who had gone to Europe the previous summer as one of ten Canadian Rangers and Cadets at an International camp, had gone ahead with Jenny's patrol to lay the ceremonial fire in a cleared spot overlooking the lake. They had pulled Chris down on a toboggan and brought a folding chair for her with an old bearskin rug to cover it. "You'll look like the Snow Queen," Jenny had giggled. "All you need is a crown on top of your parka!"

Mary Kate stood in the doorway, holding her alarm clock aloft. "Everyone just about ready? It's now six hundred seconds before midnight and Thinking Day, so we've got to hurry! Follow the trail the Daffodils made — gee, they've got big feet! — and remember what we said. No talking. Not a sound except the crunch of your feet on the snow. Stop laughing, Josie; you'll spoil it all. When the clock says midnight, Jenny's patrol will light the fire and we'll all sing 'Happy Thinking Day', then Mrs. Weston has a surprise. Make a decent circle around the fire and no pushing anyone down in the snow."

"Yes, mother," said Carol meekly. "We'll behave."

Mary Kate stuck out her tongue at Carol, then grinned. "Let's go, gang!"

In silence, the Guides reached the snow-covered beach and quickly encircled the fire. The moon shone brightly across the ice-covered lake, and Orion hung high in the southern sky. At precisely midnight, flames leaped from four sides of the prepared fire as the Daffodils touched the tinder with long matches. The Guides' voices, singing 'Happy Thinking Day', rang through the cold clarity of the winter air.

Mrs. Mac said, "It's already the 23rd in New Zealand where February 22nd comes first. Guides there greeted Thinking Day by climbing a hill at dawn and lighting a fire, before sending their wishes around the world. We like to think that we're the first Guides in Canada this year to greet Thinking Day, but perhaps somebody else is doing what we're doing at this very moment!"

Mrs. Weston opened the bag she had brought from the lodge. "Here's a giant sparkler for everyone. The Rangers will pass them around and light them for you. Be careful. Then we'll all sing 'Happy Birthday' to the World Chief Guide, Olave, Lady Baden-Powell, whose birthday it is today — the same date as Lord Baden-Powell's. Then the Patrol Leaders will place their wish sticks in the fire, we'll sing one song from each continent, and head back to the lodge and our midnight feast."

The circle of sparklers lasted through the singing of 'Happy Birthday' and all the wishes. The last one died away as the Fireweed P.L. was saying, "I wish that all Guides everywhere could visit Canada and find out what fun it is to live in a country where you have snow in winter."

After breakfast on Saturday morning, Mary Kate sat down beside Mrs. Mac. "I've just been talking to the Patrol Leaders," she said. "They're beginning to regret that they volunteered to do the breakfast dishes for the dish patrol as a Thinking Day gift. They must've talked until three a.m."

"I think twelve minutes after four would be more accurate," said Mrs. Mac. "That was the last time I looked at my watch. They weren't noisy at all, but I felt like wringing the neck of whoever was blowing up air mattresses. I wish there were enough beds to go around."

Mary Kate blushed. "That was me, actually. My air mattress holds air for about fifteen minutes. It's all right if I get to sleep first, but Jenny had a book of ghost stories, and we . . . "

"Mary Kate!" said Mrs. Weston. "You didn't encourage her!"

"Oh, she didn't need any encouragement," said Mary Kate hastily. "As a matter of fact, it was an international sort of thing." She looked at Mrs. Mac, who was looking somewhat shamefaced. "It was about famous ghosts of Scotland, and Mrs. Mac had lent it to Jenny a long time ago."

"I guess you've got me there," said Mrs. Mac. "What were you going to say before we got talking about sleep?"

"This morning we're going to do the trip to Europe because it's all outdoors. The Bluebirds are in charge and we're going to visit Scandinavia. Those who have skis will go on them and the rest of us will use the snowshoes and toboggans we rounded up. We'll be Canadians visiting Scandinavia.

"They've got things to do — like a compass trail, because they do a lot of orienteering in Sweden. There's to be a snow mountain-building contest and some other activities. It sounds really good. Breakfast was a bit late."

"Not late enough," said Mrs. Mac. "I wouldn't have minded sleeping in longer."

"I don't believe it," said Mary Kate. "I've camped with you in the summer and you're always prowling around at dawn looking for the coffee!"

"That's different. Morning should come later in the winter. Oh well, I'll survive. We're cooking lunch outside so that should work out fine."

"Then we can come back and have a rest," said Mrs. Weston soothingly. "Can we work in the other continents later this afternoon and into the evening?"

"Yes," said Mary Kate. "That's what the Patrol Leaders figured we'd do. Look, they've swept everywhere except where we're sitting and I think they're getting ready to go out. It looks like Barb's rounding everyone up."

At lunchtime, nobody turned down seconds of the hot stew. The big pot, bubbling over the fire at the beach, was soon empty.

"I don't like the look of that sky," said Jenny to Pam. "What happened to all that nice sun we had?"

"Well, at least it's milder," said Pam. "You can't complain about that."

"I'm not complaining. We had a radio on in the kitchen this morning and the weather forecast wasn't so good. They even said we might get freezing rain. Nobody else was listening and I didn't mention it because the weather forecaster said there was just a chance of it. I didn't want to worry Mrs. Mac. She might want us to leave early."

"Forget about it then," said Pam, irritably. "Ever since you got your badge about weather, you keep thinking we're going to have bad weather!"

"I do not!"

"You do so, too."

"Well, in December I was right about the thaw that spoiled our skating party. The rink was nothing but water," said Jenny. "But I won't say another word."

Back at the lodge, the Guides fell eagerly on their beds and quite a few slept. Before she dozed off, Mrs. Mac said to the Ranger in the bunk above her, "That was a brilliant idea of yours to have everyone prepare their banquet food ahead of time and bring it frozen. I don't think any of us will be fit to do more than heat it up and eat it. That fresh air and lack of sleep have tired me right out!"

By evening, everyone was well-fed and well-rested. An hour's sleep had done wonders and they had even managed to tour Asia with a relaxing hour of handicrafts, and part of Australia, before the banquet.

Outside, the temperature had been climbing steadily all afternoon and hovered around the freezing point. Wet snow had started to fall but had turned to rain. While the girls were getting ready for the evening's activities, Mrs. Mac and Mrs. Weston put on their jackets and went out on the porch.

"It seems to be changing to freezing rain," said Mrs. Weston. "I don't like the idea of slippery roads for the return trip tomorrow."

"I'm glad they've got the phone connected this winter," said Mrs. Mac. "I think I'll phone the Camp Adviser and my husband and tell them we've got enough food for an extra couple of meals if need be. I'll ask John to phone the bus driver and tell him not to come if the driving is dangerous. He can phone and let us know. Tomorrow night's the church parade with the Scouts, too. I hope the weather improves. Brrrrr! That damp's worse than the cold!"

The windows were glazed with a heavy coat of ice and freezing rain bounced off the ice-covered snow outside. The Guides sipped their hot chocolate sleepily after campfire. Barb had shown slides of the International camp she'd gone to, and the pictures of Rangers in shorts, enjoying a hot summer sun, had almost made them forget the ice storm raging around them.

"Sleep near us tonight, Barb, will you?" asked Jenny. "And tell us some more about the handsome Swedish Boy Scouts you met. D'you think I'll ever get to go to an International camp?"

"Sure, why not?" replied Barb. "You can always apply. How old are you, Jenny?"

"Almost fourteen. I'm going into Rangers this spring. Carol's getting her Canada Cord presented at the church parade tomorrow night, and so are Pam and Nancy. Do you think the bus'll be able to come for us? I don't know if I'll ever finish mine or not. Does it matter if you don't have it?"

"To go to an International camp, do you mean? No. Some of us who went had All Round or Canada Cords and some didn't. I don't even know for sure who did. What matters most is what kind of person you are — how well you get along with people, how cool you keep in an emergency, what Canada means to you, why you want to go and that kind of thing.

"When we applied, we had to write about why we wanted to go and, well, I really believe that if kids — not just kids, but grownups too — from different countries with different ways of living get together and try to understand each other, the world will be the better for it. We have to appreciate and understand each other's differences. It's easy to get along with people who act and think and eat the same as you do, but if they don't, then it's not so easy."

"Is there anything else that helps you get accepted?" asked Carol.

"Different kinds of camping experiences if it's a camp you're applying for. One thing you discover when you go camping is that you have to get along with each other and co-operate. If you don't, you have a crummy camp. You guys have been really good campers this weekend, you know. Knowing camping skills, like taking care of tents and cooking, is important. But more important is getting along with other people. If people who live in a tent are fighting with each other, it doesn't matter how neatly the tent has been pitched. It's just like the world, I guess. Beautiful houses don't matter half so much as the kind of people who live in them.

"Are you both coming up to Rangers? Somebody said you weren't, Carol".

"Well, I think I'd rather be a Cadet," said Carol. "Before I got on the basketball all-star team I was a Packie. I wasn't ever a Brownie, and it was fun helping at Brownies. I'd like to learn how to be a really good leader and Mary Kate says that's what they do at Cadets. So I can't decide whether to stay in Guides until I'm old enough to join Cadets or what."

"Why don't you come to Rangers and switch to Cadets later?" asked Barb. "We're having a canoe-tripping camp this summer . . . hey, the lights just went out!"

The electricity had suddenly failed. The girls' eyes gradually got used to the dark which was lessened considerably by the flames in the fireplace.

"There wasn't any flickering," said Mrs. Mac to everyone. "I have a feeling that we're going to be without electricity for some time. Maybe all night or even longer. That means we can't use the electric heaters, but we'll keep the fireplace and wood stove going all night. Don't waste your flashlight batteries; you may regret it if you do."

"Do you think we'll be able to get home tomorrow?" asked a small Guide anxiously.

"We hope so," said Mrs. Mac. "When I phoned my husband a little while ago, he said the storm wasn't as bad there as it sounded here. The bus driver is going to call us tomorrow if he doesn't think the road's safe enough to travel. And the Cadets have inspected the food supply and said there's enough food for four Guide-sized meals or six ordinary meals — that is what you reported, isn't it, Mary Kate? Just go easy on the water. The best thing we can all do now is to get a good night's sleep. And that's s-l-e-e-p, sleep!"

In the morning the whole outdoors shimmered and glistened. The trees hung heavily, their branches thickly coated with ice. A weak sun rose in the sky, cutting through the clouds, Mrs. Mac tried the telephone but it was dead. The electricity was still off and she was grateful for the old wood stove. To think she had once voted for its removal since it usually sat idle all summer beside the new electric one!

They decided to tidy up and get packed just in case the bus did get through. But one o'clock came and went. No bus. No phone. No electricity. It could be a long wait, but there were a lot of partly finished craft articles to work on and exploring the icy world of the campsite was fun.

They were just about to open up the grocery boxes at 3:30 when the sound of motors led everyone, shouting, to the door. "It's a sander and our bus!" shouted Sarah who got there first.

The bus driver got out of the bus and waved his thanks to the driver of the sanding truck. He said to the girls who had already started to carry supplies outside, "Did you think I'd abandoned you? I tried to phone but the lines are down all around this area. Guess your electricity was off, too! You don't look any the worse for it — you're a noisy bunch today, aren't you?"

"What are the roads like?" asked Mrs. Weston.

"Not too bad now. They've had sanders out on them all and the traffic is moving. Still lots of cars in the ditch, though!"

The trip home was uneventful. It was a rush to get bathed, have dinner, and change into uniform for the Scout-Guide Thinking Day Service, but almost everyone arrived in time.

Jenny was in the colour party, carrying the Guide World Flag. Waiting for their signal to begin, she stood beside a Scout with his flag.

"I hear you Guides went winter camping and almost didn't get back," he said. "It musta been tough last night when that freezing rain started. Did it wreck any of your tents?"

"Tents", thought Jenny, "tents". We were in a nicy, cozy building! Wouldn't you know he'd say something like that!

"Well, actually," she said aloud, "we stayed in a building — it was the first time we'd ever gone camping in winter."

"Is that right?" he said. "we do it all the time, but of course you girls . . . "

Jenny interrupted, "Next year when I'm a Ranger, it'll be different. *They* know all about winter camping and they often sleep in tents."

"OK., OK.," said the Scout calmly. "Don't get mad. Even a building in an ice storm can be scary!"

The Scouter in charge of the colour parties approached. "It's time to start, kids," he said. "Are you ready?"

Jenny clutched the staff of the World Flag tightly. "You bet I'm ready," she said.

BE PREPARED FOR HYPOTHERMIA...
BECAUSE COLD CAN KILL!

Hypothermia is the gradual cooling of the body's inner core below the normal of 37°C. and unless the cooling is reversed, can end in death.

It happens when you are exposed to cold. It happens more quickly if the cold weather is aggravated by wind or by wet. It doesn't just happen in winter. It can happen in cold water in a very short time. It can happen in wet, windy weather in spring and fall, perhaps even in cold summer conditions.

You can recognize Hypothermia if you know what to look for. As the body temperature drops, you start to shiver uncontrollably. (Shivering in itself raises the body temperature a little and added to other measures is a help.) Then the cold reaches your brain and you have difficulty speaking and the shivering comes in waves. Then you stumble and even fall, and your conversation makes little sense. Next the shivering stops, your muscles become rigid, your pulse slows down and you want to sleep. The next step is unconsciousness, then death itself.

You can prevent Hypothermia by:
— being aware of what causes it.

— keeping dry.

— wearing proper clothing in cold weather. Wool is best because it is warm even when wet. Wear layers of clothing: thermal underwear, woollen shirts and sweaters, wool or down jacket, corduroy or wool slacks, several pairs of wool socks, lined boots, wool hood, or hat and scarf, wool mitts. Carry extra socks, mitts, sweater.

— wearing waterproof boots and if there's *any* threat of rain, having adequate rainwear and putting it on before you get wet.

— eating lots of high-energy food — fats and carbohydrates (sugar and starches) which give you energy quickly, and protein which gives you long-lasting energy. Snack on nuts, candy, raisins or gorp (see Inbetween 4).

— carrying an emergency shelter such as a plastic sheet, space blanket, or tube tent.

— keeping moving at the first sign of hypothermia. Doing isometric exercises will help. Don't sit around in the cold or wet.

— appointing a responsible person to keep a special lookout for signs of hypothermia and agreeing to follow that person's directions.

You can start treating Hypothermia by:
— preventing further loss of body heat by warming the victim with the body heat of others; lighting a fire; supplying warm fluids; sheltering the victim and if wet, carefully replacing wet clothing with dry. If the victim is unconscious get help as fast as possible but don't leave her alone.

SOME TIPS FOR WINTER CAMPING

Take enough warm clothing.

Read section on Hypothermia.

Make sure you have some experienced winter campers with you, especially if you are going to use tents.

Use an arctic-type sleeping bag: or two ordinary sleeping bags, one inside the other: or two wool blankets inside an ordinary sleeping bag. Remember to have at least as much under you as you have over you. Cold comes up from below very quickly.

Don't go to bed in the clothes you have been wearing. Change into warm, dry night clothes.

Keep your feet warm. A hot water bottle is a good idea as long as you are sure it won't leak.

It takes ten cups of snow to make one cup of water. Melting ice is better. Snow and ice are apt to be polluted so purify the water by boiling it for 20 minutes or by using water purification tablets.

Sleeping on snow heats it up and may even melt it somewhat. Make a bed of evergreen boughs, or use a thick layer of newspaper, covered with a ground sheet.

Tent pegs cannot be pounded into frozen ground or snow. Use logs to hold the guy lines down or tie to trees.

If you are laying a fire in the snow, trample the snow down hard and lay a foundation of green logs on which to build your fire.

Know how to recognize frostbite and how to treat it.

Beware of water covered with thin or unsafe ice.

Eating snow or ice may result in painful cracking of the lips.

Building a snow wall can help protect you from the wind. Wind increases the cold tremendously.

Enjoy winter by using your common sense.

NATURE'S SUPERMARKET

Long before there were supermarkets or ordinary markets, people grew and raised their own food. Before they farmed, they simply looked for and gathered their food in the wild. Some people still do. You have to be sure you know what you're looking for, lest you eat something poisonous. There are many good books on the subject. Here are some foods which are easy to find in the wild.

Milkweed: Collect young milkweed pods, about 6 cm. long. Boil them in salted water for 5 or 6 minutes, pour off the water and boil them again in fresh boiling water. Drain, add pepper and butter and you have a delicious vegetable.

Cat-Tail: Parts of the cat-tail can be gathered and eaten the year around. In spring, the stem has a crisp, white core that can be boiled like asparagus or eaten raw. The immature flower spike can be eaten like corn-on-the-cob later on. Remove the papery husk and boil in salted water for 5 or 10 minutes. The ripe flower head is covered with yellow pollen. You can shake or rub it into a bowl. Substitute half the flour in a pancake or muffin recipe with the pollen and make cat-tail muffins or pancakes. In winter, if you dig up cat-tail roots, you can dry them and grind them into a meal and use for cat-tail porridge or as a partial flour substitute.

This very useful plant has other handy parts. The long leaves, if collected when green, can be hung to dry, then dampened and used as weaving material. Have you ever seen a rush seat on a chair? It was a cat-tail! The seeds (and this is also true of milkweed seeds) make good stuffing for pincushions or pillows. Dry cat-tail pollen is also a good fire starter. Try it sometime.

Staghorn Sumac: Collect the big, purplish-red flower heads and soak them in cold water until they turn pink. Then strain the water through a fine cloth or sieve, add sugar and you have pink "sumachade". Some people enjoy it hot, too. You can also substitute unsweetened sumach juice for any other fruit juice in a jelly recipe.

Birch: Do you know that you can tap a birch tree for its sap just as maple trees are tapped? Birch sap runs a little later than maple, but it runs more quickly. It's not as sweet as maple and you may want to add sugar or honey before drinking it.

Find out what edibles grow wild in your locality. If you live near the ocean, you will find a rich harvest there that inland dwellers don't have.

THINKING DAY

Can you imagine how surprised Olave Soames must have been when she discovered that her birthday, February 22nd was also the birthday of the man she was to marry, Robert Baden-Powell? The world of Guiding decided to mark this coincidence by calling it 'Thinking Day' and celebrating it by having parties with an international flavour, sending Thinking Day cards and greetings around the world, and with special church services.

In 1932, a Belgian Guider at the World Conference in Poland, suggested that Guides everwhere give 'a penny for their thoughts', and thus was born the World Thinking Day Fund and the idea of 'Thinking Day pennies'. The Canadian World Friendship Fund is used to support the World Thinking Day Fund, to help send Canadian Guiding representatives to International events, to bring others who could not otherwise afford it to Canada, to help develop Guiding in countries where Guiding is struggling, to help maintain the World Centres, and to give assistance to our sister Guides in times of national disasters.

Some companies remember the Canadian World Friendship

Fund all year around by bringing an extra penny a week for the purpose. Sometimes they have special fun ways of collecting Thinking Day pennies for some weeks before February 22nd.

— Measure your waist, or the outline of your foot, and bring the equivalent in pennies.

— Make an outline of something symbolic of another country on a piece of cardboard and tape pennies to the outline.

— Make a decorated bank and fill it with pennies.

— Cover the trefoil on your company's World Flag with pennies.

— 'Write' the names of a member country in pennies.

Can you think of some other ways? Write them down and share them with your company.

MEMBER COUNTRIES OF THE WORLD ASSOCIATION OF GIRL GUIDES AND GIRL SCOUTS

At the 22nd World Conference of WAGGGS in 1975 there were 94 member countries, most of them Full Members, the others Associate Members, (marked * on the list below) working towards the responsibilities of Full Membership.

Argentina
Australia
Austria
Bahamas*
Bangladesh
Barbados
Belgium
Benin, Peoples Republic of (Dahomey)*
Bolivia*
Botswana*
Brazil
Burundi*
Cameroon*
Canada
Central African Republic*
Chile*
China, Republic of
Colombia
Costa Rica*
Cyprus*
Denmark
Dominican Republic*
Ecuador*
Egypt, Arab Republic of

El Salvador
Ethiopia*
Finland
France
Gambia, The*
Germany
Ghana

Greece
Guatemala
Guyana
Haiti
Iceland
India
Indonesia*
Iran
Ireland
Israel
Italy
Ivory Coast*
Jamaica
Japan
Jordan*
Kenya
Korea
Kuwait
Lebanon
Liberia
Libya*
Liechtenstein
Luxembourg
Madagascar*
Malaysia

Malta
Mauritius*
Mexico
Monaco
Netherlands
New Zealand
Nigeria

Norway
Pakistan
Panama, Republic of
Paraguay*
Peru
Philippines
Portugal
Rhodesia
Sierra Leone
Singapore
South Africa
Spain
Sri Lanka
Sudan
Surinam*
Swaziland*
Sweden
Switzerland
Tanzania
Thailand
Togo*
Trinidad & Tobago
Turkey*
Uganda*
United Kingdom of Great Britain & Northern Ireland

United States of America
Upper Volta*
Uruguay*
Venezuela
Vietnam, South*
Zambia*

Can you find them all on a map of the world?

You don't have to leave Canada
for an international flavour

Have you ever met a member of Guides Catholiques du Canada (secteur français)? They have been affiliated with Girl Guides of Canada — Guides du Canada since 1962. They recognize the same Chief Commissioner as the head of Guiding in Canada. However, they have their own programme, uniform and literature to suit their needs as French-speaking, Roman Catholic Guides.

The Brownies, from 9 to 11 years of age, are called Jeannettes. The Guides (the word is spelled the same but pronounced in the French manner) are from 12 to 14, and Kamsoks (Rangers) are from 15 to 17.

Their Guide programme is based on 'travels' in five 'countries':

Gar-o-mour — the land of physical fitness

Verte Sente — the land of environmental concerns and camping

Cap-Able — the land of the arts

Plaine de Trucs — the land of communications

Au Pays d'aujourd'hui — the land of today in one's community, in education and in Guiding

Guides Catholiques are encouraged to choose the activities they wish to do, just as you are, and they try to keep a balance of the five 'countries'.

This is their Promise and Law, in French and in English:

Promise: Avec vous toutes, confiante sans le Seigneur, je m'engage
— à rendre les autres plus heureux
— à servir avec audace mon pays
— et à partager l'idéal de toutes les guides du monde.

With you all, trusting in God, I promise
— to make others happier
— to serve my country boldly
— and to share the ideals of Guides around the world.

Law: *La Guide face à elle-même:*	*A Guide looks at herself:*
La guide est vraie et joyeuse.	A Guide is honest and happy.
La guide est accueillante et fraternelle.	A Guide is welcoming, warm and friendly.
La guide acquiert la maîtrise d'elle-même.	A Guide practises self-control.
La guide surmonte les difficultés.	A Guide overcomes difficulties.
La guide aime la nature.	A Guide loves nature.
La guide face aux autres:	*A Guide looks at others:*
La guide vit et fair vivre.	A Guide lives and lets live.
La guide merite et fait confiance.	A Guide is trustworthy and trusts others.
La guide partage l'effort de tous.	A Guide is co-operative.
La guide rend service.	A Guide gives service.

La guide face au Seigneur: *A Guide looks at God:*

La guide apprend à vivre avec   A Guide learns to live with
le Seigneur.   God.

Do you know how to sing 'O Canada' and 'Taps' in French? If you don't, look up the words in *Songs for Canadian Girl Guides* and learn them.

Find international flavour in your own community

Do you have some neighbours who came to Canada from another country? Ask them to tell you about the country they came from. They may give you some recipes, teach you a song or a dance, show you their national dress, tell you what life there was like. Invite them to visit a Guide meeting.

Look in a food store, or any kind of store, and see how many items came from other countries. Do you know what Canada exports to other countries?

What about your own family tree? Have you ever made one? You start with your name and where you were born; then your parents and their parents and so on, back as far as you can go. If your people are Indian or Inuit, Canada will probably be the birthplace no matter how far back you go. But if you're not, at some point you will find an ancestor who came to Canada from another country. Find out what you can about that country. Perhaps you have something around your house from that country. If you're lucky, you will even know how to speak more than one language. That's a tremendous advantage, because it lets you communicate with many more people.

If you're not a Canadian citizen, and want to become a Guide, you make the Promise, substituting after 'duty to God' these words: 'to my own country and to the country in which I am a guest' for 'the Queen and my country'. If you transfer to Canadian Guiding from another country in which you were enrolled, you need not be re-enrolled. You may wear the pin with which you were enrolled or the Canadian Tenderfoot pin. You may wear badges you earned in your own country or the equivalent Canadian badges if the requirements are similar.

Would you like to write to a Guide in another country?

Send your name, full mailing address and age or date of birth to:

The International Post Box Secretary,
Girl Guides of Canada,
50 Merton Street, Toronto,
Ontario   M4S 1A3

She will try to link you with a pen pal in another country.

Some international games

Rhodesian Clapping Game: You will find this in a very useful, small book, *Games from Many Lands for Brownie Guides and Guides*, available from the Distribution Centre.

Mulambilwa: Two teams of five to nine players kneel, facing each other. In front of each player is a small ninepin, or plastic bottle. (The African uses a large berry or makes his own ninepin.) At a signal, each player throws a small ball at the ninepins of the opponents. The balls are picked up quickly and thrown again at the opposing side. This rapid throwing back and forth is continued until all the pins on one side are knocked down. The vanquished players then run towards a goal that has been previously designated by the leader. Those caught before they reach the goal must pay a forfeit.

Match My Feet: Sometimes this game is played in a circle with one person who is 'It'. While those in the circle clap their hands rhythmically, 'It' stands in front of someone and does some steps in rhythm with the clapping. The person she faces must imitate her exactly. If she fails to do this, she becomes 'It' and proceeds in the same manner with someone else. If she imitates 'It' successfully, 'It' moves on to someone else and tries again.

Sometimes sides are chosen for this game. Each side sends one of its members to be 'It' on the opponent's side. In this case, 'It' cannot leave any opponent in line until that opponent makes a mistake. The side whose 'It' gets to the end of the opponent's line first wins.

International Camp

Equipment: Slips of paper with the names of member countries of the World Association of Girl Guides and Girl Scouts. There should be one less slip than the number of players. A list of the countries used is kept by the game leader.

To Play: The players stand or sit in a large circle, with one player blindfolded in the middle. All, except the centre girl, have the name of a country. The game leader, using the master list, calls out two countries in this way:

"Guides from Denmark are camping in Korea". The players

with 'Denmark' and 'Korea' attempt to exchange places, shaking each other's left hand en route, before the blindfolded person touches either one. If she is successful in touching one, the touched person becomes the centre player. If 'International Camp' is called, all players change (shaking hands) with someone else.

OUR 'NEIGHBOURS' IN SPACE

Do you ever stand and look at the sky on a clear night? Can you pick out and name some of the constellations? Do you know the names of the other planets? Do you know how far away they are? The distances sound impossible, don't they? Do you know that the light which enables you to see Polaris, the Pole Star, left that star about the time that Christopher Columbus was sailing across the Atlantic? That's how long its light has taken to reach Earth.

These charts will help you recognize some constellations

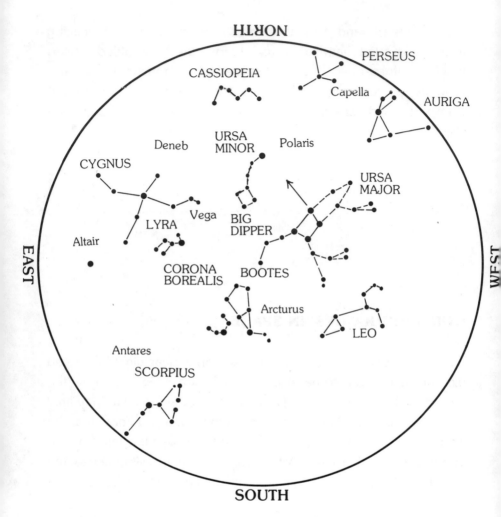

SOME MAJOR CONSTELLATIONS AND BRIGHT STARS FOUND IN THE SUMMER SKY

They are visible in these positions at 45° latitude in early June at 9.00 p.m. (Standard Time) and early July at 7.00 p.m.

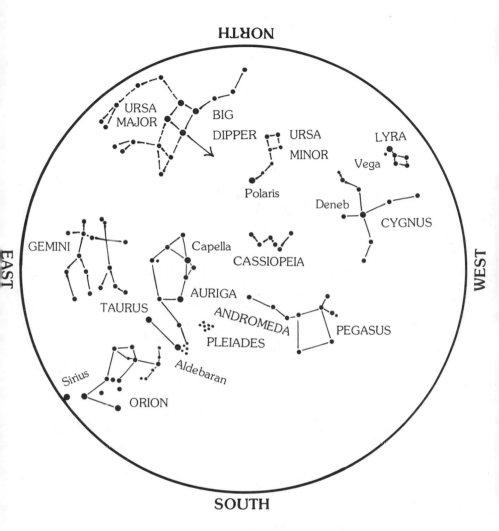

SOME MAJOR CONSTELLATIONS AND BRIGHT STARS FOUND IN THE WINTER SKY

They are visible in these positions at 45° latitude in early December at 9.00 p.m. and in early January at 7.00 p.m.

The stars constantly shift westward. They rise and set four minutes earlier each night, gaining about two hours a month throughout the year.

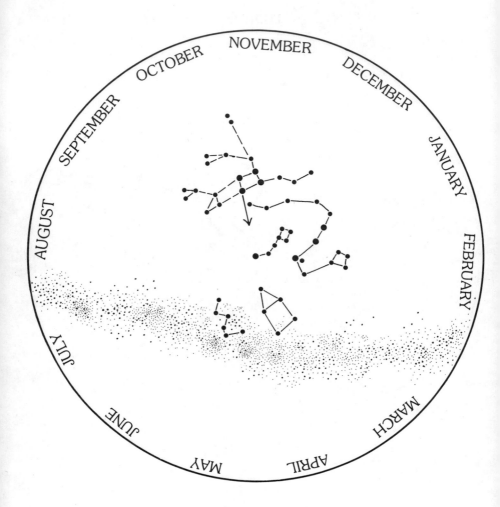

NORTH CIRCUMPOLAR CONSTELLATIONS

Face north and hold this chart over your head so that the current month is toward the north. This will show you how these constellations, which are always visible in all parts of Canada, appear at about 9.00 p.m. Standard Time.

The shaded section is the Milky Way.

APPENDIX

POSTSCRIPT

You have made many discoveries about yourself as you travelled along the four paths at home, in your community, at camp and in the outdoors, and in the world at large. Best of all, you are prepared to keep on discovering. The Promise you made at your enrolment is yours for life.

What will you do now?

Join a Ranger group and look wider still?

Join a Cadet company and train for leadership in Brownies or Guides?

Leave Guiding?

The choice is yours!

What you have learned in Guides will help you grow up to be a responsible, creative woman who is able and willing to help the world become a better place.

Someday, you may decide to come back to Guiding as an adult leader and help girls of the next generation to catch some of the fun and adventure you have enjoyed.

> "May the road rise to meet you;
> May the wind be always at your back;
> May the sun shine warm upon your face
> and the rain fall soft upon your fields;
> And may the Lord hold you in the hollow
> of His hand."
>
> —old Gaelic blessing

YOUR PERSONAL RECORD OF BADGES AND EMBLEMS

Do you want to keep a record of the badges you are working on, or have earned? The list which follows is from the 1975 edition of *Guiding for You*. Check the latest edition and add any new badges or note any name changes. *Guiding for You* outlines the requirements for each badge and emblem. Your Guider may want the tester to sign completed sections of badges.

BADGES

NAME OF BADGE	I'VE DONE THESE SECTIONS	I'VE EARNED THE BADGE
Aircraft		
Aquarist		
Art Appreciation		
Artist		
Astronomer		
Athlete		
Backyard Camper		
Backyard Cook		
Baker		
Basket-Maker		
Baton Twirling		
Bee Keeper		

NAME OF BADGE	I'VE DONE THESE SECTIONS	I'VE EARNED THE BADGE
Bird-Watcher		
Boatswain		
Camp Leader		
Campfire Leader		
Canoeist — Bow Paddler		
Canoeist — Stern Paddler		
Canoeist — Voyageur		
Challenge		
Child Care		
Citizen		
Collector		
Conservationist		
Cook		
Creative Crafts		
Creative Drama		
Cyclist		
Dairymaid		
Dancer		
Dancer on Skates		

NAME OF BADGE	I'VE DONE THESE SECTIONS	I'VE EARNED THE BADGE
Ecologist		
Emergency Helper		
Explorer		
Fire Safety		
First Aid (Stage II)		
First Aid (Stage III)		
Fisherman		
Flower Arranger		
Folklore		
Friend to the Handicapped		
Gardener		
Globetrotter		
Gymnast		
Handywoman		
Health		
Heritage		
Hiker		
History		
Homemaker		

NAME OF BADGE	I'VE DONE THESE SECTIONS	I'VE EARNED THE BADGE
Home Nurse		
Horsewoman		
Hostess		
Industrial		
Interpreter		
Junior Camper		
Keep-Fit		
Knitter		
Landgirl		
Laundress		
Leather Worker		
Lifesaver		
Lifesaver Helper		
Metal Worker		
Mineral Collector		
Musician		
Music Appreciation		
Naturalist		
Native Lore		

NAME OF BADGE	I'VE DONE THESE SECTIONS	I'VE EARNED THE BADGE
Needleworker		
Outdoor Adventure		
Outdoor Cook		
Pathfinder		
Pet Keeper		
Photographer		
Postal		
Poultry Farmer		
Public Speaker		
Rabbit Keeper		
Reader		
Reporter		
Rescuer		
Scribe		
Seamstress		
Signaller		
Singer		
Skater		

NAME OF BADGE	I'VE DONE THESE SECTIONS	I'VE EARNED THE BADGE
Skier		
Snowshoer		
Spinner		
Stalker		
Swimmer		
Team Sport		
Thrift		
Toymaker		
Tracker		
Water Skier		
Weatherman		
Weaver		
Wilderness Camper		
Woodman		
World Trefoil		
Writer		

Emblems

NAME OF EMBLEM	WHEN EARNED
Aquatic	
B.P. (Be Prepared)	
Camping	
Challenge	
Craft	
Fine Arts	
International	
Little House	
Physical Fitness	
Woodlore	
Religion in Life	

BIBLIOGRAPHY: A LIST OF BOOKS TO HELP YOU

These books are available from Girl Guides of Canada, Distribution Centre, 50 Merton Street, Toronto, Ontario M4S 1A3, or from your nearest agency which sells Girl Guide supplies. Your Guider receives a catalogue each year which contains the current price and tells you how to order. Some of these books you may want to buy yourself. Others should be part of your patrol or company libraries.

New books are often added to the catalogue and sometimes books become no longer available, so be sure to check with a current catalogue before you order.

Programme:

Guiding for You	contains the requirements for the Tenderfoot Test and all badges and emblems; Guide uniform; history of Guiding in Canada.
Policy, Organization and Rules	contains the rules for camping, hiking, boating, etc. and tells you how Guiding is organized and carried out in Canada.
Scouting for Boys	B-P's own book that started it all, has lots of ideas and yarns, especially for outdoor activities.

Song Books:

Jubilee Song Book	Canada's own collection of all kinds of songs.
Songs for Canadian Girl Guides	an older collection than *Jubilee*, but a good one.

Diamond Jubilee Songbook	forty songs from the British Girl Guides.
Girl Guide Song Book 1 and Girl Guide Song Book 2	more songs from the British Girl Guides.
Girl Scout Pocket Song Book	a collection from the Girl Scouts of the United States of America.
Our Chalet Song Book	a book of songs often sung at Our Chalet in Switzerland, in English and in other languages.

Game Books:

Boum!	contains different kinds of games and helps you make up your own.
Guide Games and Recipes	has games from different countries. Recipes, too!
Games from Many Lands for Brownie Guides and Guides	has games from eighteen different countries.

Guide History:

Like Measles — It's Catching!	was how Lord Baden-Powell described Guiding. This book, written by Anne Gloin has excerpts from girls' diaries, tells about many exciting happenings in Canadian Guiding from the beginning. Lots of pictures, too.

Baden-Powell, Chief Scout of the World — by Wyatt Blassingame tells the story of the Founder's (Lord Baden-Powell's) life.

B-P's Life in Pictures — B-P's exciting adventures told through 'comic strips'.

Camping:

Camps and Holidays — by Elizabeth Robertson, has lots of information about camping skills.

Your Own Book of Campcraft — by Catherine T. Hammet, has lots of illustrations.

Hiking:

Backpacking — by R.C. Rethmel has almost everything the backpacker needs to know.

Food for Knapsackers and Other Trail Travellers — by Hasse Brunnelle is a handy, pocket-sized book of lightweight foods and cooking tips.

Map and Compass:

Your Way with Map and Compass — (Teacher's Book and Student's book) both give you step-by-step information on orienteering and lots of practical exercises to try.

Be Expert with Map and Compass — by Bjorn Kjelstrom, is more advanced than the previous book, but clearly written with lots of things to do.

International:

Trefoil Round the World	has lots of information about the World Association, tells you about Guides and Brownies in every country which is a member of WAGGGS, and gives you each country's Promise, Law and Motto.
Olave Baden-Powell	by Elizabeth Hartley, has lots of pictures of our Chief Guide, Lady Baden-Powell and her many adventurous visits to Guides all over the world.
The Story of the Four World Centres	has pictures and the history of each of the World Centres, Our Cabaña, Our Chalet, Olave House and Sangam.
Charts of Girl Guide/Girl Scout Pins	show you, in full colour, all the Tenderfoot pins or Promise badges of Guides around the world.

Prayers:

Readings and Prayers for Guides	suitable for company camp and private use.

Knots:

Knots for Everybody	is a pocket-sized, folding card with directions and illustrations of all the common knots and hitches.
Knots and How to Tie Them	is a very clearly written book of knots, hitches, and splices with very good pictures.

Nature:

Fifty Trees of Canada   by J. L. Van Camp has pictures and a description of 50 common Canadian trees.

Birds   by Zim and Gabrielson has pictures and descriptions of many birds.

Public and school libraries, and bookstores, have many other books which you will find interesting and helpful. Look for the Golden Nature Guides, for books of craft ideas, for biographies of interesting people, for adventure stories. Browse in a library and make your own discoveries.

Check the most recent Girl Guide Distribution Centre catalogue for any new publications.

374

Author: Dorothy Crocker

Design and Production: William Fox/Associates

Illustrations by:

Leoung O'Young —   Cover, 9, 13, 17, 18, 19, 33, 35, 36, 39, 40, 51, 61, 64, 69-74, 79, 87, 100, 111, 114, 126, 129, 134, 163, 170, 172, 174, 182, 217, 230, 233, 235, 245, 246, 247, 249, 252, 254, 261, 289, 301, 303, 321, 324, 336, 361.

Helen Fox —   10, 14, 16, 21, 24, 27, 37, 43-48, 76, 78, 89, 92, 107, 110, 116, 128, 136, 138, 140, 142, 143, 145, 147, 149, 150, 153, 155, 157, 159, 161, 187, 189, 192, 199, 201-214, 228, 239-243, 267, 276, 279-281, 343-346, 348.

Credits and Acknowledgements

"Match My Feet" and "Mulambilwa", from "Fun and Festival from Africa" by Rose Wright, © Friendship Press, New York, 1967. Used by permission.

"Sussex Campfire Opening" printed by permission of Mary Chater.

"Eengonyama" reprinted from "Scouting for Boys", by Baden-Powell, "Scout Brotherhood Edition", published by the National Council, Boy Scouts of Canada.

"Daylight Taps" words by Olave, Lady Baden-Powell.

Girl Guides of Canada — Guides du Canada gratefully acknowledges the assistance given by the Boy Scouts of Canada.

Girl Guides of Canada — Guides du Canada gratefully acknowledges the many people across Canada who contributed to the development of the Guide Handbook, including girls, leaders, members of national standing committees and the staff of National Headquarters.

INDEX

MY FRIENDS' ADDRESSES
AND PHONE NUMBERS

FAVOURITE RECIPES

CAMP RECORD

MY BRIGHT IDEAS

382

AUTOGRAPHS

NOTES